Icelandic
Folk
and Fairy Tales

Icelandic Folk and Fairy Tales

Selected and translated with foreword
and notes by May and Hallberg Hallmundsson
Illustrations by Kjartan Gudjónsson

FORLAGIÐ

Icelandic Folk and Fairy Tales
English translation © May and Hallberg Hallmundsson
Illustrations © Kjartan Guðjónsson
Printing: Oddi, Iceland 🦢

1st edition: Iceland Review 1987
2nd edition: Almenna bókafélagið 2007
3rd edition: Forlagið 2009
Reprinted 2010

Forlagið · Reykjavík · 2010

ISBN 978-9979-53-517-1

www.forlagid.is

Contents

List of Illustrations

Foreword

Nowhere does a nation bare its soul to the same extent as in its popular lore, its folktales. In the aggregate, such stories will tell all. They contain the people's loftiest yearnings and deepest fears, their most ardent passions and hopes, their truest beliefs. They reveal their sense of honor, valor, and humor, their flights of imagination, their creative force — in short, the whole of their humanity as fashioned by the land in which they live.

Icelanders are generally very attached to their country, perhaps more so than most other peoples. And by that we do not mean patriotic pride in the nation's achievements or chauvinistic flag-waving on holidays (although that is by no means absent either) but rather a love for the land itself in its physical presence, for its soil, mountains, streams, valleys, even its fire-spewing volcanoes and frozen wastes of ice. For eleven hundred years, they have been fostered by this land, which has alternately chastened and emboldened them, teaching them perseverance and humility, resourcefulness and patience. To the Icelanders, the land was never just an accumulation of inanimate matter — a pile of stones here, a patch of earth there — but a living entity by itself. Each feature of the landscape had a character of its own, revered or feared as the case might be, and such an attitude was not a far cry from believing that it was actually alive, or, at the very least, full of life; traces of that belief still linger. Life, in fact was abundant everywhere: in hills, rocks, mounds, lakes, mountains. Sometimes, it was invisible to ordinary human eyes; so, for example, were Eve's unwashed children, the elves (*Genesis of the Elves*, page 14). But when the magistrate's wife of Burstarfell (page 18) looked at the familiar rock formations in the land around her, having daubed a smidgeon of elfin ointment in her eye, she "saw that all that was quite different from what it appeared to be. It was all farms, houses, and large villages, filled with people..."

Other forms of life, however, couldn't make themselves so conveniently scarce — and a good thing it was, too! Poor Gissur of

Botnar (page 34) wouldn't have stood much of a chance had the trollwife of Búrfell been as quiet and unobtrusive as the elves. It was, of course, hard to imagine that creatures of such tremendous physical stature as the trolls could be easily hidden, and for the Icelandic mountains no lesser life seemed appropriate; anything smaller would have been dwarfed.

Also the waters, both salt and fresh, were teeming with life, and not only with fish. Although some of the meaner water sprites might lose their lives in dealings with enterprising humans (*The Hired Hand and the Lake Dwellers*, page 25), others, of different disposition, would fare better (*Of Marbendill*, page 29). And all these creatures had human qualities imputed to them. They could be as benevolent or as malicious as any human being, equally vulnerable ("Pain's felt by all, even the troll," *Hallgerdur of Bláfell*, page 36), and similarly in need of help and companionship. Even the seals in the sea were more or less human under their skins (*The Sealskin*, page 94) — a belief that will not surprise anyone who has ever looked into a seal's eyes.

Yet if the folktales are revealing of people's attitude toward the land and how natural features were personified, they are even more so of the conditions under which people in Iceland lived during the centuries. In the long subarctic winter nights, when the only source of light would be tiny fish-oil lamps ("*Give Me Back My Bone, Gunna,*" page 44), or at best some tallow candles, it was not hard to imagine that there were ghosts in every corner, especially when the literature with which people were entertained during these nights was chockful of ghost stories. In such dark and gloomy surroundings, any perceived sound or movement whose source might not be immediately identified, could be attributed to specters and fetches, or other occult beings. Thus, some of the ghost stories might be interpreted as a cry for more and better light. As a matter of fact, Thomas Alva Edison is probably the greatest "ghostbuster" of all times, for with electrification, the once thriving ghost population has definitely become an endangered species.

In times of hardships, people would dream of hidden valleys among the interior mountains, where life was so much better than what they were used to that visitors would be served wine as a matter of routine (*Bjarni Sveinsson and His Sister Salvör*, page 84; *Úlfur's Lake*, page 78). Descriptions of sheep's milk thick with cream (*Visitation by the Bishop of Skálholt*, page 89) are the testimony of people who have known hunger first hand and crave fat-rich foods. Similarly, the discomfort of cramped quarters in the Icelandic *badstofa*, where people worked and slept, two in each narrow bed, may be seen in the wishful depiction of a separate sleeping hall with roomy, individual beds (*Visitation...*). One can almost hear the "Oh-if-only!" sigh behind the words. And even more to the point, it is quite likely that the incest at the heart of the story would never have happened had it not been for such close accommodations.

Such things and many more may be gleaned from the folktales. They hide nothing from the probing mind. Reading them, just as the poet Stephan G. Stephansson said of the Icelandic quatrain — also very much a folk medium — "you've got in your hand to hold / the history, country, nation."

Although the systematic collection and recording of Icelandic folktales began only in the last century, the stories themselves have roots as old as the people who shaped them. It might even be argued that they are older, for some of the motifs clearly hark back to early Germanic times, cf. the "ling snake" in *The Serpent of Lagarfljót* (page 96). The Icelandic saga literature is likewise replete with episodes and motifs that belong to the folk tradition, although they have been inserted into a larger context and given a literary form that often surpasses that of the typical folk story. One is reminded, for example, of the Glámr episode in the *Saga of Grettir*, the Fróðá marvels and hauntings in *Eyrbyggja Saga*, and the vision of Dörruðr toward the end of *Njál's Saga*. To this list also belongs the delightful story in Snorri Sturluson's *Heimskringla* of the four guardian spirits who thwarted the first foreign takeover attempt of Iceland, that of King Haraldr Gormsson of Denmark. According to the tale, the king sent his henchman, a sorcerer who assumed a whale's shape for the journey, to Iceland on a spying mission in preparation for an invasion. But in each quarter of the country, as he tried to go ashore, the emissary was confronted with one of the guardian spirits accompanied by a host of related creatures. Thus denied landfall all around the country, the sorcerer turned back, reporting to King Haraldr that the venture he had in mind was not feasible. The story clearly has a motif in common with one of the tales of Saemundur the Learned (*How Saemundur Got His Benefice*, page 60). And if the four guardian spirits — a vulture, dragon, bull, and giant, all now securely ensconced in the

Icelandic coat of arms — remind an attentive reader of the symbols of the four Christian evangelists, so much the better, for it shows how the folk imagination molds and adapts materials to fit its own purpose and time.

But the masters of the sagas apparently didn't think it worthwhile to write down and preserve these folk stories for their own sake outside the frame of larger narratives. So they lingered on the lips of the people, told over and over again, changed, varied, and expanded. Some initial endeavors at recording folktales were made by Jón Gudmundsson the Learned (1574-1658) and a few of his contemporaries, and the general antiquarian interest of the 17th century later spurred others in the same direction. The great Icelandic manuscript collector Árni Magnússon (1663-1730) collected folktales along with everything else, although he tended to relegate them to a status inferior to the sagas. A few other collectors and recorders worked in the 18th century, but it was only after the Brothers Grimm published their *Kinder- und Hausmärchen* — popularly known as "Grimm's Fairy Tales" — in 1812-15, that a systematic approach was applied to the collection of folktales, both in Iceland and the other Nordic countries. Thiele published his *Danske Folkesagn* (Danish Folktales) in 1818-23 and Asbjørnsen and Moe their *Norske Folkeeventyr* (Norwegian Folk and Fairy Tales) in 1845. That same year, two Icelandic scholars, Jón Árnason and Magnús Grímsson, began methodically to amass tales, poems, riddles, and maxims in Iceland. By 1852, they had acquired enough to publish a small volume of *Íslenzk æfintýri* (Icelandic Fairy Tales) while continuing to gather more materials. In this task, they were greatly encouraged by a German scholar, Dr. Konrad Maurer, who himself compiled stories in Iceland in 1858 and published them in his own translations as *Isländische Volkssagen der Gegenwart* (Present-day Icelandic Folktales; Leipzig, 1860). Dr. Maurer held out the possibility to his two Icelandic colleagues that their collection might also be published in Germany. And this was indeed what happened. Like Maurer's book, and with his help, it was printed in Leipzig and appeared in two volumes in 1862-64. Unfortunately, Grímsson had died in 1860, just on the threshold of seeing the fruit of his labors, so it fell to Árnason alone to prepare the collection for print. It is for that reason that the tales are generally known only under his name. They are recognized by every child in Iceland as "Jón Árnason's Folktales."

Árnason continued to uncover more stories until his death in 1888, at which time he left behind an enormous amount of additional materials. His entire collection, six volumes, including an index, was published in Reykjavík, 1954-61, under the editorship of Árni Bödvarsson and Bjarni Vilhjálmsson. Although several other scholars followed with creditable collections, most notably Ólafur Davídsson (*Íslenzkar þjóðsögur*, 1895) and Sigfús Sigfússon (*Íslenzkar þjóðsögur og -sagnir*, 1922-58), it is from Árnason's storehouse alone that the translations in the present volume have been made.

Taking his cue from Dr. Maurer, Árnason divided his compilation into nine distinct categories: 1) Mythical Tales 2) Ghost Stories 3) Tales of Sorcery 4) Nature Stories 5) Legends 6) Historical Tales 7) Stories of Outlaws 8) Fairy Tales and 9) Humorous Tales. (To this, he added 10) Maxims, or Old Wives' Tales.) In this volume these categories have been, for convenience's sake, condensed into four: *Elves and Trolls*, containing stories from Árnason's 1); *Ghosts and Sorcerers*, featuring tales from his 2) and 3); *Saints and Sinners*, comprising tales from categories 5) and 7); and *Miscellaneous Tales*, which have been taken from the remaining 4), 6), 8), and 9). All but one of the stories are from Árnason's original collection, which makes up the first two volumes of Bödvarsson and Vilhjálmsson's expanded edition. Only the last tale, *"Now I Should Laugh —"* (page 113), which we considered a superior variant, has been taken from volume V of the latter.

About the choice of tales, we needn't add many words. A selection is always more or less subjective, although in fact some of the stories included have earned such a preeminent place in Icelandic folklore that they could hardly be ignored in a representative anthology. We began the process several years ago, before the publication of the German and French sister volumes, edited by Messrs. Hubert Seelow and Regis Boyer, respectively. Their two editions contain the exact same stories. We were, however, selecting materials for a different reading public, so while our choices in many cases have coincided with theirs, we took a slightly different turn. In that, as alluded to earlier, we were motivated primarily by the wish to give our readers a fuller understanding of life as it was lived in Iceland for a thousand years. In a few instances, this may have resulted in a choice of tales containing somewhat similar features, but we hope that it has been offset by the greater variety of detail from which an attentive reader can glean an insight into the life of the people during their long centuries of isolation and perseverance. The final judgment on whether or not we have succeeded in our purpose must, of course, rest with the public.

In conclusion, a note on the translation seems to be in order.

We have not, as some other translators have done, tried to make our English version a totally faithful, or even as-close-as-possible, rendition — warts and all — of the Icelandic text. Such an attempt, we thought, would only make the translation an oddity, awkward to read and unidiomatic. Nor did we, since this is a popular and not a scholarly edition, see any point in it. Although most of the stories are well told, and some excellently, few are remarkable primarily for their stylistic brilliance or literary flair. They are generally written in the everyday spoken Icelandic of the time when they were recorded, many of them taken down word for word as told by the storytellers, who often were unschooled men and women — farmers, laborers, housewives, maids. With no pretensions to literary skills, these people would obviously be more interested in the contents than the packaging. The best way to render such narratives into English, we concluded, would be in plain, unadorned prose that was faithful to the meaning, if not to every word of the story. So, wherever the original text is bumpy or awkward — and it is in many places — we tried to smooth it over, and we did not hesitate to reshape or switch sentences around if we thought it was inducive to a clearer understanding or a more straightforward narrative. Similarly, we sometimes left out repetitious or unneeded phrases which did nothing to forward the story. We did not, however, retell any of the tales or add stylistic flourishes. We still consider them true translations of the originals.

Aside from sharing more than half of the tales with the German and French editions, this English version has one other aspect in common: the excellent illustrations by Kjartan Gudjónsson. One of Iceland's most eminent artists, Mr. Gudjónsson (b. 1921) is known both as a painter and a master illustrator, and his interpretations of the tales are both apt and illuminating. Forceful, humorous, awe-inspiring, or bitter-sweet as the case may demand, his pictures add a new dimension to the stories that enhances them by assuming their spirit.

New York, July 1986   May and Hallberg Hallmundsson

Elves and Trolls

Genesis of the Elves

Once upon a time God Almighty paid a visit to Adam and Eve. They greeted him warmly, showed him all around their house, and presented their children to him. God thought they were very promising. Then he asked Eve if they had any other children besides those he had met. She said no. As it happened, however, Eve hadn't quite finished washing some of her children, and she was ashamed to let God see them that way; for that reason she concealed them. This was not unknown to God, and he said, "Whatever must be hidden from me, shall also be hidden from people."

The unwashed children then became invisible to human eyes, and they lived in hills and mounds and rocks. From them, the elves are descended, while humans are the descendants of those of Eve's children whom she presented to God. Elves can never be seen by human beings unless they want to be. They, in turn, can both see humans and make themselves visible to them.

The Field Hand

A man from the Sudurnes, in the Southwest, once went to the North to find summer work as a field hand. As he reached the heathlands, such dense fog descended upon him that he lost his way. It was followed by sleet and cold, so he decided to stop and pitched his tent. Having done that, he broke out his food and began to eat. While he was enjoying his meal, a rust-colored dog entered the tent, all wet and hungry-looking. The southerner was surprised to see a dog in such a place where he expected no living creature. And so ugly and outlandish was the animal that the man was a bit frightened of it. Nevertheless, he gave the dog all it wanted to eat. The mutt wolfed down the food and then left, disappearing into the fog. The man didn't bother his head about it but, having had his fill, lay down to rest with his saddle for a pillow.

When he had fallen asleep, he dreamed that a woman entered the tent. She was of large stature and advanced in years.

14

"I want to thank you for my daughter, my good man," she said, "although I can't reward you as you deserve. But I'd like you to accept this scrap of a scythe, which I'll put here under your saddle. I hope it will be of some help to you, for it will remain equally sharp whatever it cuts. Never heat it in a fire, for then it will be of no use, but you can hone it if you feel the need to."

Then the woman disappeared.

When the man woke up, he saw the fog was gone and it was bright daylight, the sun high in the sky. The first thing he did, then, was to get his horses and prepare to continue his journey. He then folded his tent and began to load and harness the animals. But when he picked up his saddle, he saw a scythe, rather worn and rusty but still usable. Then he remembered the dream, and he packed the implement. With that, he set off again and had a good journey: He soon found his way and was quick to reach the nearest human settlements.

As he came to the northern parts, however, no one would take him on for it was almost a week into the haymaking season, and all the farmers had hired whatever help they needed. Then he heard said that there was a woman at one farm in the district who had not yet taken on any field hand. She was a wealthy woman and thought to "know" a good deal. She didn't usually hire help and never began her haymaking until a week or two behind all others, and yet she was always finished as soon as they were. The few times she had engaged field hands, she would keep them for a week only and never pay any wages. Thus cautioned about her, the southerner was directed to this woman. And since he could find no work elsewhere, he went to her and offered to mow her fields. Accepting, she said she would let him stay for a week. "But I'll pay you no wages unless you mow more during that week than I can rake Saturday," she warned him.

The man thought this was a bargain and started mowing. He used the scythe the elf woman had given him and found that it cut well. It never needed honing, and he kept mowing for five days. The woman treated him well, and he was most satisfied.

At one time, he happened into the smithy and, to his surprise, saw a huge number of rakes and a big heap of snaths. He thought to himself that his mistress certainly wasn't lacking in implements.

Friday night he went to sleep as usual. Then, during the night, he dreamed that the elf woman who had given him the scythe came

16

to him, saying, "You have cut a great deal of grass, but it won't take your mistress long to rake it all together, and if she catches up with you tomorrow, she'll dismiss you. So, if you think this is going to happen, then go to the smithy, take as many snaths as you please, and tie scythes to them, then bring them out to the field with you and see how it goes."

So saying, the elf woman disappeared, and the field hand awoke. He lost no time getting up and once again began mowing. About mid-morning, the woman came out carrying five rakes.

"You have cut quite a lot, and more than I thought," she said. Then she placed the rakes here and there in the mown grass and began raking. The field hand noticed that while the woman raked a good deal, the other rakes did even more, although he saw no one holding them.

As mid-afternoon approached, he saw that the grass he had already mown would not suffice. He then went to the smithy, picked up several snaths, and tied scythes to them. That done, he returned to the field and scattered the implements about the unmown grass. All immediately started swinging, so the cut part now grew quite rapidly. And thus it went all day until evening, and there was still more cut grass to rake.

When the evening came, the woman went in, taking her rakes with her. Asking the field hand to come along and carry the snaths home, she said he knew more than she had expected and that deserved a reward; he could stay with her as long as he wanted, she said.

The field hand remained there for the rest of the summer, and they got along very well together. They made a lot of hay, even at a leisurely pace. In the fall, she paid him very handsome wages which he took with him to the South. He returned to her the following summer and all the subsequent ones that he worked as a field hand.

Later, he acquired his own farm on the Sudurnes, and he was always thought to be a good man. He was an excellent fisherman and an energetic worker whatever he did. Always alone when mowing his field, he never used any other scythe than the one the elf woman had given him. Yet he never lagged behind others in his haymaking. He had, however, nothing more to mow than his home-field, as is the rule in those parts.

One summer it happened, while he was at sea fishing, that a

neighbor came to his wife asking that she lend him a scythe; he had broken his, he said, and was quite desperate. The woman went looking among her husband's implements and found the good blade, his one and only. She lent it to the farmer but warned him not to heat it in fire, which she said her husband never did. This he promised and went back home.

Here, he tied the scythe to his snath and started mowing, but not a single blade of grass would fall. The farmer got angry and honed the scythe, but it didn't help. Then he went to his smithy intending to beat out the edge, for he figured there wasn't much to lose though he heated the old scraper. But as soon as it was in the fire, the scythe melted like wax, turning into a mere heap of slag.

The farmer then went back and told the woman what had happened. She became frightened, for she knew her husband would be extremely upset when he learned about it. And that was indeed the case, although he did not long brood over it.

But how he missed that scythe!

The Magistrate's Wife of Burstarfell

There once lived at Burstarfell in Vopnafjördur a rich county magistrate of a good family. He was married and maintained a generous household.

It was customary at Burstarfell during the winter that people take a nap in the early evening before the lamps were lit in the *badstofa*; it was up to the magistrate's wife how long the nap would be. She would light the lamps herself and awaken the people.

One evening it happened that the magistrate's wife didn't wake up at her usual time, and the working people got up by themselves and kindled the lights. The magistrate didn't want to have her awakened; he said she was dreaming and should be allowed to enjoy it. It was far into the evening when she finally woke up, heaving a weary sigh, and told her dream.

She had felt, she said, that a man came to her and asked her to get up and go with him. She did as he asked, and he took her some distance from the farm to a large boulder that she recognized to be in the Burstarfell land. The man walked three times clockwise around the boulder, at which time it appeared to her that it turned into a small but elaborate house. He then led the magistrate's wife into the house, which was beautifully furnished. There she saw a woman in the throes of labor and having great difficulty. Also present in the house was an old woman but no other people.

The man now explained his visit to the magistrate's wife. He had come to ask her to save the woman in childbed, who was his wife. She would die, he said, unless she had human help.

The magistrate's wife went over to the would-be mother and said, "The Lord Jesus help you."

These words worked such change that the woman soon delivered, to the great joy of everyone. The magistrate's wife noticed, however, that after she mentioned the name of Jesus, the old woman who was also there dragged herself off her bed and carefully swept out the whole house. The visitor had the feeling that the old one considered the dwelling soiled by the utterance of that name.

The baby now had to be washed, and the magistrate's wife was asked to do that. The mother then gave her a jar filled with ointment, with which she asked that the baby's eyes be daubed during the bath. The magistrate's wife, believing the ointment must be something salubrious, did so. It also occurred to her that she ought to smear some in her own eyes but was afraid to do so in view of the others. She did manage, however, to touch her right eye very quickly with her fingertip unseen.

The bathing was soon finished, and the magistrate's wife prepared to return home. As she departed, the mother gave her a most exquisite cloth; it was the finest velvet and all embroidered with gold. The man escorted the magistrate's wife back outside and walked three times counterclockwise around the house, whereby it once again turned into a boulder. He then accompanied her home to Burstarfell, where he took his leave of her.

The magistrate's wife now produced the cloth from her pillow and showed them all the proof of her story. No one had ever seen anything of the kind, and people say the cloth is still used as an altar cloth in the parish church to which Burstarfell belongs.

As for the magistrate's wife, she felt a change in her right eye, which she had daubed with the ointment, for she was now able to see everything that happened in the earth as well as on it. Close to Burstarfell, there are said to be large rock formations and high cliffs. The magistrate's wife saw that all that was quite different from what it appeared to be. It was all farms, houses, and large villages, filled with people who behaved just like anybody else, mowing, raking, and cultivating fields and meadows. They had cattle, sheep, and horses, all of which grazed with other livestock. And the people similarly mixed with other people, working at whatever they pleased.

But no one saw this except the magistrate's wife, and she noticed that these people used much more practical work methods and were much keener in forecasting weather than ordinary people. They often tedded their hay even when the weather wasn't dry, and sometimes they did not, although there was strong sunshine and breeze. She also noticed that whenever they tedded, dry weather followed but rain if they didn't. Other kinds of work adhered to a similar pattern. The magistrate's wife tried to learn from their example and methods and felt it always worked out for her benefit.

Some time now passed without event.

Then one day the magistrate's wife went to town, and when she stepped into the store she saw the woman she had once helped in childbirth behind the counter. She had gathered up and held in her arms a load of selected dry goods — some of the best the merchant had on his shelves. The magistrate's wife realized that no one other than she was aware of the woman's presence, so she walked over to the counter and said in her friendliest tone of voice, "Well, finally we see each other again."

The elf woman turned around, looking quite angry, and without a word spat in the right eye of the magistrate's wife. With that, she lost sight of the elf woman and never saw her again. Nor could she ever after that see anything more than she had before she smeared the ointment in her eye.

The Tunga Bluff

In olden times, many hundred years ago, a very rich farmer lived at the farm of Tunga in Saelingsdalur, in the West. He had several children, of whom two sons appear in this story. Their names, however, are no longer known, and we shall call them Arnór and Sveinn. Both were men of promise, though each in his own way. Arnór was a brawny, spirited youth, while Sveinn was quiet and reserved ànd no stalwart at all. They were equally different in temperament. Arnór was a merry fellow and often played games with other youths in the valley, who would meet by a bluff by the river opposite the farm of Tunga; it was called the Tunga Bluff. In winter, it was their favorite sport to slide on the hard snow down the bluff — for it was very high — onto the sand flats below, and there would often be quite a ruckus, with shouts and clamor, around Tunga Bluff in the twilight. As a rule, Arnór was the loudest.

Sveinn seldom went along with them. He would most often go to church when the others went out playing, but he would also go off by himself and then frequently linger by the Tunga Bluff. Rumor was that he had dealings with the elves that lived in the bluff, and one thing was certain: Every New Year's Eve he would vanish, and no one knew what became of him.

Sveinn often admonished his brother not to make so much noise on the bluff, but Arnór made fun of him, saying he wouldn't weep for the elves if the racket bothered them. He carried on as before, despite Sveinn's repeated warnings that he would be responsible if anything happened.

Then it occurred one New Year's Eve that Sveinn disappeared as usual, but this time he was away longer than he had ever been before. Arnór said he would go and look for him; he felt sure he would be with the elves in the bluff.

Arnór went off, walking in the dark, for it was quite overcast, and he soon reached the bluff. The next thing he knew, he saw the bluff open up on the side facing the farm, revealing countless rows of shining lights. At the same time he heard some lovely singing and understood that the elves were conducting a mass. Moving closer to see what was going on, he came to what looked like the open doors of a church and a multitude of people inside. A priest in beautiful vestments stood before the altar with many rows of lights on each side.

Arnór went in through the door and saw his brother Sveinn kneeling at the altar rails; the priest had his hands on his head and seemed to be pronouncing something. It was Arnór's understanding that Sveinn was being ordained in some way, for there were many other men in vestments all around. He called out, saying, "Come, Sveinn, your life is at stake."

Sveinn, startled, stood up and looked back toward the door; he seemed about to run to his brother. But at that moment, the one at the altar cried out, "Lock the doors of the church, and punish the human who has disturbed our peace." Turning toward Sveinn, he added, "And you, Sveinn, will have to leave us, for which your brother is to blame. And because you stood up to go to your brother, respecting his impudent call more than holy ordination, the next time you see me here in these vestments, you shall be stricken dead."

Arnór watched as the other vested men lifted Sveinn up high, and he disappeared through the stone vault of the church. At that moment, a pealing sound of bells rang out, and a great commotion began inside as everyone scrambled to the door.

Arnór ran out into the darkness as fast as he could, but as he was heading home he heard the elves galloping with a clatter of hoofbeats behind him. As he ran on, he heard the loud chant of one of the riders:

> "Ride, let us ride.
> The hills in darkness hide.
> Craze him and race him,
> the wretch, off the way,
> so he never may
> see the light of day,
> never see the sun of another day."

The whole flock of them then raced between Arnór and the farm, cutting him off, so he had to turn away. Having reached the slopes south of the farm and east of the bluff, he gave up and sank down exhausted, and the entire flock rode over him. They left him lying there more dead than alive.

As for Sveinn, he returned home after bedtime. He was very depressed and would tell no one what had happened, except to say that they had better look for Arnór. The search continued all night long, but he was not found until a farmer from Laugar, who was on his way to morning prayer at Tunga, came upon him by chance on the slopes. Arnór was very far gone but still conscious; he told the farmer the whole story of the evening before as it has been recounted here. He said it would be no use nursing him, for he would not survive. He died there on the slopes, which ever since have been called Death Slopes.

Sveinn was never the same after this event. He grew even more solemn and somber, and never was he known to go near Elfin Bluff again, nor even to look in that direction. He abandoned all worldly affairs, took holy vows, and joined the abbey at Helgafell. So learned was he that none of the brethren equalled him in erudition, and his chant was so lovely that no one had ever heard the like in beauty.

His father lived at Tunga until old age. When he was well along in years, he became very sick. This was close to Holy Week. Suspecting where he was heading, he sent a message to Sveinn, asking him to come and see him. Sveinn reacted quickly but left word at Helgafell that he might not return alive.

He reached Tunga on the Saturday before Easter. His father was by then so weak that he could barely speak. He asked his son to sing a mass on Easter Sunday, giving instructions that he be carried to the church; he said he wanted to die there. Sveinn was reluctant to do this, but he did on the condition that no one open the church during mass; his life depended on it, he said. People thought it a strange request, but some ventured the guess that he still didn't want to look in the direction of the bluff. The church at that time stood on a hill far up in the hayfield east of the farm, and the bluff was in plain view from the doors of the church.

The old farmer was carried to church as he had directed, while Sveinn put on his vestments before the altar and began the mass. All those present agreed that they had never heard such lovely singing or such masterful chanting, and they all sat there, as it were, numbstruck. But when the priest finally turned from the altar and began to chant the words of blessing over the congregation, a sudden violent windstorm from the west flung open the doors of the church. This startled the congregation, and people turned around to look toward the door. There in plain view, then, was the bluff, its side open like an entrance and emanating a brilliant light from countless rows of candles. When people turned to the priest again, however, he had sunk down and had already expired. This was a great shock to everybody, especially since the old farmer had, at the same time, fallen dead off the pew on which he had lain, facing the altar. The weather both before and after the sudden squall was quite calm, so it was obvious to all that the windstorm from the bluff had not been accidental.

Present at the mass was the farmer of Laugar, who had found Arnór on the slopes before, and he told the whole story. People then realized that the elf bishop's prediction had come true, for as the bluff stood open and the doors of the church were flung up wide, the two entrances were directly opposite each other, so the eyes of the elf bishop and Sveinn met as they chanted their blessings; it is a peculiarity of elf churches that their doors face in the opposite direction of those of human churches, that is, toward the east.

A parish meeting was later held about this matter, at which it was decided that the church be moved down from the hill into a hollow by a brook closer to the farm. By that arrangement, the farm lay between the bluff and the church, so the priest has never since had an unobstructed view from the altar through the church door to Elfin Bluff. Nor have any similarly calamitous events happened since.

"Father of Eighteen in Elfland"

It happened on a certain farm one summer that all the people were out in the fields except the lady of the house. She was at home, doing her chores, along with her three-year-old son. Up to that time, the boy had grown and developed well. His speech was already fluent, and he was intelligent and exceptionally promising.

Now, since the woman had her household work to do besides looking after the child, the time came when she had to leave him alone temporarily while she took the milk troughs to a nearby brooklet to wash them. She left the boy in the doorway. But when she returned, shortly afterward, and spoke to the child, he cried and howled in an angry, wretched manner, the like of which she had never heard before. Previously, the boy had been very even-tempered and of a gentle, obedient disposition, but all she got out of him now was ugly screams and howls.

This went on for some time. The child never uttered a word and was so fretful and peevish that the woman didn't know how to react to this change in his behavior. What's more, he stopped growing and began to behave like a dunce.

All this grieved the mother, and in her desperation she went to see a woman nearby, who had a reputation for prudence and knowledge, recounting to her the misfortune that had befallen her. The neighbor asked how long ago precisely the child had first displayed this peculiar behavior and how she thought it had come about. The boy's mother told her everything as it had happened.

When the wise neighbor had heard all the circumstances, she said, "Hasn't it occurred to you, my dear, that the boy might be a changeling? In my opinion, he has exchanged while you left him alone in the doorway."

"I don't know," said the mother. "Can you tell me how to find out for certain?"

"I think I can," said the neighbor. "Leave the child unattended some day, and make sure that he comes across something that is an absolute novelty to him. He is sure to say something if he sees no one around. But you'll have to eavesdrop to learn what he says, and if you find the boy's speech strange and suspicious, then spank him without mercy until something happens."

With this, the two women broke off their talk, and the boy's mother thanked her neighbor for the good advice. Back home, she placed a small, eared pot in the middle of the kitchen floor, then took a few broomsticks and tied them together, end to end, until the upper part reached all the way through the kitchen chimney, while at the lower end she tied a stirrer, letting it stand in the pot. Having contrived this gimmick, she took the boy into the kitchen and left him there. She herself went outside and hid behind the door, where she could see and hear through the crack between the jamb and the door.

After a short while she saw that the child began to toddle around the stirrer in the pot, examining it closely. Then he said, "I'm as old as witness my whiskers, a father of eighteen in Elfland, but never in my life have I seen a pole so long in a pot so tiny."

Hearing this, the woman returned to the kitchen with a hefty piece of birch, took the changeling, and whipped him long and hard, while he howled most dreadfully. After she had birched him for a while, she saw a strange woman enter the kitchen, a beautiful little boy on her arm, whom she kept kissing and cuddling. The stranger said, "How differently we behave. I fondle your child, while you beat my husband."

So saying, she put down the boy, the woman's son, leaving him there, and took her husband with her. They both disappeared instantly. The boy grew up with his mother and became a fine man.

The Hired Hand and the Lake Dwellers

There once was a rich farmer. Housing on his farm was both spacious and well maintained, the *badstofa* all paneled and with a wooden floor. There was one great drawback, however: Whoever remained at home on Christmas Eve would be found dead the morning after, and for this reason the farmer found it difficult to retain his hired people; no one wanted to stay at home that night, although somebody had to.

Once, as so often before, the farmer hired himself a new shepherd, for he had a huge herd of sheep and needed a vigorous man to tend to them. The farmer told the young man honestly about circumstances at his farm, including the drawback mentioned before, but the shepherd avowed he paid little heed to such nonsense and declared himself just as willing to enter the farmer's service for all that. The farmer then hired the man, and a mutual liking was soon established between them.

Time now passed, and Christmas Eve arrived. The farmer and his household then prepared to go to services — all except the shepherd; he did not. The farmer asked him why he wasn't changing, to which the hired hand answered that he was going to stay home; it was not right, he said, to leave the farm unguarded and let the animals go that long without any attention. The farmer begged him not to bother about that. He reminded him what he had told him before, that nobody was safe in the house on Christmas Eve because any living creature found inside it would be killed; he said he would not under any circumstances take that risk once more. The shepherd dismissed all that as superstition and said he wanted to try. When the farmer could not persuade him by any means, he left along with his other people, and the shepherd remained behind alone.

Once everybody was gone, the young man began to ponder and plan what to do. Thinking that something must be amiss, he felt he had better be prepared for whatever might happen. The first thing he did was to light candles all around the *badstofa* so it was brightly lit. Then he started looking for a place to stay.

Finally, he pried out two panels from the gable end of the room, eased himself in through the opening, and put the panels back in place, so that nothing could be seen. There he stood between the turf wall and the paneling, but through a crack between the boards he could see all around the *badstofa*. His dog lay asleep under one of the beds.

Some time after the hired hand had thus settled in his hiding place, he saw two men, both strangers and none too pleasant-

looking, enter the room. They looked all around it, and one of them sniffed.

"Smells of humans. Smells of humans," he said.

"No, there's nobody here," answered the other.

Then they took lights and searched everywhere, both high and low, around the *badstofa* and finally found the dog under the bed. They took the animal, quickly broke its neck, and threw out the carcass. The hired hand praised his good luck for being where he was, for he realized that he wouldn't have had a prayer against those two.

After this, the *badstofa* filled with people. They put up tables and covered them. All their table settings were of silver, the plates as well as the knives and spoons. Then they loaded the tables with food and sat down to dine. These people had a roaring good time and made merry, eating, drinking, and dancing all night long. Two guards were posted to keep track of any human traffic and to watch for the break of day. They went out three times during the night, reporting back each time that they hadn't seen anybody about and that it was still not daybreak.

When the shepherd judged that daybreak must be near, he decided to take things into his own hands. He grasped the two loose panels, jumped out on the floor behaving wildly, banging the panels together and roaring at the top of his lungs, "Daybreak! Daybreak!"

The strangers were so startled at this that they all scrambled to the door, one over another, leaving all their belongings behind — the tables, the silverware, and the clothes they had doffed during the night while they were dancing. Some of them were injured, while others were stampeded to death. The hired hand chased them and kept slamming his panels together and shouting, "Daybreak! Daybreak!" until they reached a lake near the farm. There, all the people jumped in and vanished, and the shepherd then realized that they were lake dwellers, or water sprites.

After this, the hired hand returned to the house, dragged out the dead, killed those who were still alive, and burned the corpses. Then he cleaned up the house, took all the silverware, clothes, and other things and put them aside. When his master arrived, he showed him everything and told him the whole story of what had happened. The farmer said he was a man of great good luck that things had turned out so well for him. The hired hand took half of everything the lake dwellers had left, giving the rest to the farmer; it was a considerable fortune.

The hired hand remained with the farmer several more years, made money hand over fist, and became a well-respected man. Never again were there any more strange happenings at the farm on Christmas Eve.

Of Marbendill

On the southwestern peninsula south of Reykjavík there is a small farming village called Vogar — Creeks — but actually the full name of it is Kvíguvogar — Heifer Creeks — and it is so called in the *Book of Settlements*. In early times, there was a farmer in Vogar who was an avid fisherman, for even today the place is one of the best in southern Iceland for small-boat fishing.

One day, as so often before, the farmer went out angling. There is no mention of his catch of fish that day, but he did get something very heavy on his hook, and as he hauled in the line, he saw the shape of a man emerge and pulled it aboard. The farmer saw that the man was alive and asked him how he happened to be there in the sea. The other told him he was a marbendill — that is, a merman — from the seafloor. Asked by the farmer what he had been doing when he was hooked, Marbendill replied, "I was fixing the cowl of the chimney on my mother's kitchen." And he added, "Please let me down again."

The farmer told him there was no chance of that for the time being. "You'll stay with me," he said, and there was no more talk between them, for Marbendill avoided any conversation.

When the farmer was good and ready, he went ashore, taking Marbendill with him. After he had pulled up his boat, his dog came running to greet him and jumped up at him excitedly. Annoyed, the farmer kicked the dog away. That's when Marbendill laughed the first time.

As the farmer was heading up through his hayfield to his house, he stumbled over a hummock and cursed it. Then Marbendill laughed the second time.

When the farmer reached his house, his wife came out to meet him and greeted him most lovingly. The farmer responded fondly to her caresses. That's when Marbendill laughed the third time.

Turning to the merman, the farmer said, "You have laughed three times now, and I am curious to know why."

"There's no chance of that," said Marbendill, "unless you promise to take me back to the fishing grounds where you pulled me in."

The farmer promised to do so.

"I laughed the first time," said Marbendill, "when you kicked your dog, which was so sincerely glad to see you return. I laughed the second time when you stumbled over the hummock and cursed it, for that hummock is a treasure trove full of gold mint. And I laughed the third time when you responded so fondly to your wife's fawning welcome because she is false and unfaithful to you. Now, keep your promise, and take me back where you caught me."

"As of now," replied the farmer, "I have no way of checking the validity of two of the things you mentioned, that is, my dog's love for me and the faithlessness of my wife. But I will test your truthfulness and see if there is money hidden in the hummock. If that proves correct, there is more likelihood that the two other statements are true, too, and I will keep my promise."

The farmer now went and dug up the hummock, finding a great deal of money as Marbendill had predicted. Without another word then, the farmer launched his boat and took the merman back to where he had pulled him in. Before he was lowered into the sea, however, Marbendill said, "You have done a good deed in returning me home to my mother, and you may be sure that I'll reward you if you keep your eyes open and seize the opportunity. And now farewell, my good farmer."

The man then let Marbendill loose in the deep, and he is out of the story.

Shortly after this happened, the farmer was told that seven sea-gray cows had been seen on the foreshore adjoining his homefield. Losing no time, he grabbed a stick of wood and went down there to look at the animals, which were restless and rushed about, to and fro, on the foreshore. The farmer noticed that they all had a sac on their muzzle, and he surmised that unless he could burst the sacs, he would lose the cows. He then struck one of them on the muzzle with the club he had in his hand and managed to capture it. But the others were lost to him, for they immediately jumped into the sea.

The farmer felt certain that it was Marbendill who had sent him the cows as a token of gratitude for his freedom, and the one he captured was indeed the most precious animal that ever grazed in Iceland. A great breed of cattle descended from her has since spread over most of the country; called the sea-cow breed, it is distinguished by its gray color.

As for the farmer, he remained a man of great good fortune all his life. It was he who added to the name of his community, calling it Kvíguvogar instead of plain Vogar, after the cow that had emerged on his land.

> The time is well remembered
> when Marbendill laughed of yore,
> how fawning sweet the mistress
> when her man came ashore,
> kissing him and fondling,
> perfidious to the core.
> The foolish man distrusted
> and kicked his dog therefore.

Drangey Consecrated

The island of Drangey lies approximately midway between the head and mouth of Skagafjördur but much closer to the western shore than the eastern one. It is so named because it is flanked by two free-standing cliffs (Icel. *drangar*), one on the seaward side of it — and that one is said to have almost totally crumbled some 80 years ago — and the other on the south side. Two narrow straits separate both from the main island. Like the two *drangar*, the island itself is a solid rock whose perpendicular cliffs, more than 500 feet at their highest, in some places rise straight out of the sea, in others from a strip of a foreshore, as is the case on the west side. Nowhere can the island proper be ascended without ladder or rope; this is known from the *Saga of Grettir* and may also be inferred from the previously mentioned altitude of the cliffs.

On top, the island is extremely grassy and so extensive that it is thought to equal the homefield at Hólar in Hjaltadalur, which is supposed to be 96 days' mowing. The grass on the island is now utilized in one way only: In the fall, the owners place sheep on it for grazing, and the animals will feed there all winter long unless it be a very severe one. A point on the southeast of the island derives its name from this custom and is called Lambhöfdi — Lamb's Head.

No one has permanently resided on Drangey since Grettir and his brother dwelt there. In some ways, in fact, it is not very inhabitable, since it is devoid of fuel, except for a little driftwood. Nevertheless, the island is not without its good parts, and it is usually crowded in the spring. Then people flock there both for catching birds — inexhaustible in the cliffs around the island — and also for fishing.

Before Grettir came to Drangey, it was a common, but after he was killed (about 1030), it passed to the episcopal see of Hólar in Hjaltadalur, so the bishops had authority over the island and the most to gain from bird and fish catches. But the catching of birds was not without its disadvantages in those times, for Drangey, as earlier noted, appears to be a sheer rock out of the sea on all sides, from whatever angle one looks at it. To begin with, while there were still courageous and enterprising catchers in the country, they would eagerly go down the cliffs in ropes and without much caution, for the bird was incomparably greater then than it is now, and this frequently resulted in terrible fatal mishaps. The men would fall from their ropes as they were lowered, be torn open in the plunge, and land on rocks so that every bone in their bodies was broken.

But people quickly noticed that the best equipped catchers would perish on the cliffs just as soon as those who had inferior ropes, and that did not appear to be quite natural. Their lines, when pulled up, were cut through as if they had been either hacked with an ax or severed with some other kind of cutlery, and people even thought they heard pounding in the cliffs immediately before the men plunged from their ropes or just when the lines snapped. The popular consensus was that the cliffs were inhabited by some beings who did not want the mainlanders to take all the catch out of their hands and who felt they had no less claim to the island's yield than the trespassers.

For a long time, there was no relief for the continuing fatalities, and a point was reached when people began to recoil from going to the island as often as in former times. This went on until Gudmundur Arason the Good became bishop of Hólar. Bishop Gudmundur, as well known from his saga, was a great utilizer of holy services and sanctifications, by which he often brought relief and abatement of ailments to his countrymen and disposed of many evil spirits. He was kind to the destitute and not only took many of them in at the see when he was there but also brought many of them home with him when he traveled about the country. For this reason, there were sometimes shortages at the see in the spring, and provisions had to be found wherever possible. He frequently sent his workers to Drangey in the spring, both for fishing and bird-catching, and it was soon evident that the spirits of the island were equally adverse to the bishop's men as to others. This led to a great loss of lives.

Informed of what was happening on the island, the bishop decided to go there with his clerics and holy water. In Uppgönguvík — Ascent Inlet — there is a stone ledge that looks as if it were man-made, and it is called Gvendur's Altar. When the bishop disembarked, it is said he sang mass using this ledge as an altar, while others say he only said his prayers there. And it has since been a custom, observed even today, that no one ascend or descend Drangey without saying his prayers at this ledge.

That done, Bishop Gudmundur went about and consecrated the island, beginning slightly north of Haeringshlaup in the southwest, below which the sheds now stand, and continuing to the right, or counterclockwise, both high and low. And wherever he couldn't get at it from the foreshore, he would do so by sea and by having himself lowered down the cliffs. In this manner, he and his clerics went all around the island with benedictions and chants and holy water.

It is not known that he had any encounters with evil spirits until he was back again to the west of the northern corner of the island, close to Uppgönguvík. There he had himself lowered down the cliff as in many other places, and when he was as far down as he thought appropriate, he began his consecration and benedictions. But he had been at it only a short time when a large hand, gray and hairy in a red sleeve, emerged from the rockwall, holding a big, sharp-looking saber which it put to the rope the bishop was dangling on and immediately severed two strands of it. What saved the bishop's life was that the saber couldn't cut the third strand, for it was thoroughly consecrated. At that moment, the bishop heard a voice from the cliff saying, "Bless no more, Bishop Gvendur. The wicked need a place of their own, too."

The bishop then had himself pulled up, declaring that he would not consecrate the rest of the cliff, from that point to Byrgisvík. But, he said, he felt that no harm would come to his servants or to anybody else from then on in those parts that were already sanctified. And that is said to be true to this day. The section of the cliff that Bishop Gudmundur left unconsecrated still remains that way. It has since been called Heidnaberg — Pagan Crag — and it is said to have a greater concentration of birds than all the rest of the Drangey cliffs. So strong does this belief continue that men rarely have themselves lowered down Heidnaberg.

The guardian spirits had an early hunch that Bishop Gudmundur would be a difficult adversary. After his predecessor, Bishop Brandur Saemundsson, died (1201), a certain trollwife was visiting at Fljótahorn in the North. She shouted over to another trollwife, located at Strandhali, declaring in a voice exultant with relief and so loud that it was heard in all the intervening parts, "Now the bishop of Hólar is dead!"

But the trollwife at Strandhali replied, "Someone will follow who won't be any better, and that's that Gvendur."

Gissur of Botnar

The far upland part of the Rangárvalla County on the western side is called the Land or Land Country. In the earliest times of settlement, it was probably a beautiful district, well suited for farming, but it has since become quite denuded owing to the eruptions of Mt. Hekla, which lies due east; only the river of Western Rangá and a few ridges separate the two. The farm of Naefurholt, which long was the uppermost settlement east of the Rangá proper, used to be located among those ridges, but it was destroyed by the 1845-46 eruption of Hekla. The Western Rangá flows close to the ridge where the farm now stands, and a short way from it, there is a mountain named Bjólfell. Farther upstream, and a good distance above any human habitations, a great chasm cuts northeastward into the ridges. It is rimmed by cliffs on both sides but opens up to the northwest and down to the Rangá proper. This chasm is called Tröllkonugil — Trollwife's Canyon.

In the extreme upper part of the Land, above Land Forest, the earth is very eroded and sandblown. This area is called the Kjallaka Tongues, and it extends far into the mountain pastures between the rivers of Thjórsá on the west and Rangá on the east, even up above the head of the Rangá. Up there, it is practically a sandy wasteland, and it is quite narrow between the streams. Mount Búrfell stands west of the Thjórsá, facing the Kjallaka Tongues across the river.

In olden times, two trollwives made their homes in these parts, one in Bjólfell and the other in Búrfell. They were sisters and got on well together, so the one in Búrfell often went east across the rivers to see her sister in Bjólfell, and it may be assumed that the other one reciprocated, although there are no records of that.

Búrfell is very rocky, with sheer cliffs on all sides. About midway off its eastern side are two flat-topped rocks, not too high, on either side of the Thjórsá, and between them, in the river itself, there are two free-standing rocks just about the same height as the others, so that the river at this point runs in three channels. The story goes that these stepping stones were put in the river by the trollwife of Búrfell, so she wouldn't have to wet her feet when she went to see her sister but could jump across in three leaps. The rocks are since known as Tröllkonuhlaup — Trollwife's Leap.

The common trail for all those who travel north to the mountain pastures lies along the Kjallaka Tongues, no matter whether they are going to round up sheep, fish, hunt for swans, or dig up roots. Such trips were very common in the old days during the summer, for the area boasts not only some of the very best fishing lakes in the country — actually called Fishing Lakes — but also a great multitude of swans all around and plenty of angelica in many places.

Toward the lower end of the Land Country, there is a farm named Botnar, more commonly called Laekjarbotnar. At the time of this story, it was inhabited by a farmer named Gissur.

Once in the summertime, he went up to the mountain pastures to fish, traveling with one pack horse besides his mount. When he felt he had caught enough for the horse to carry, he broke camp and set off for home.

Nothing worth telling happened until he reached the Kjallaka Tongues by Trollwife's Leap. Then he heard a terrifying voice calling out of Búrfell:

"Lend me a pot, sister!"

An equally terrifying answer sounded back from Bjólfell:

"What do you want with it?"

And the trollwife of Búrfell answered:

"Cook a man in it."

"And who might he be?" asked the one in Bjólfell.

The other replied, "Gissur of Botnar, Gissur of Laekjarbotnar."

At that moment Gissur looked over to Búrfell and saw the troll-wife scrambling down the mountainside heading straight for Troll-wife's Leap. He then felt convinced that she intended to carry out her words and that he had better make all the haste he could to save his life. Letting go of the pack horse, he gave the whip to his mount, which happened to be an outstandingly swift animal, never looking back nor reining in his horse — just riding as fast as it would go. Nevertheless, he sensed that the trollwife was gaining on him, for he heard her panting ever closer behind him. He took the straightest route down the Land with the trollwife on his heels, and it was his luck that the people of Klofi saw his race with the troll-wife as the two of them reached Mark Heath. They reacted instantly because they saw there was no time to lose and rang all the church bells at Klofi as Gissur got inside the homefield fence.

Having lost Gissur, the trollwife threw her ax after him, and as he reached the door at Klofi, his horse fell down dead under him, the blade of the ax sunk up to the shaft in its loin. Gissur praised God for his deliverance.

The trollwife, on the other hand, was so jolted by the sound of the bells that she went mad and ran off again as fast as she could. She was seen from various farms in the Land Country heading far east of her native parts in the direction of Trollwife's Canyon. She was found there dead a few days later, and the canyon has ever since been named for her.

Hallgerdur of Bláfell

There was a man named Ólafur, said to have been from Eyja-fjördur. He went south to Stafnes every winter season to work as a fisherman. Then it happened once, as Ólafur was southward bound across the mountains, that it began to snow. The snowfall soon became so heavy that he totally lost his way and went about for a long time not knowing where he was going — until he recognized a landmark: a mountain named Bláfell. Then, through the snow-fall, he saw an enormous trollwife not too far away. She accosted him, saying:

"Ólafur Mouth,
are you going south?
You should well fare
with your fat mare.
Wry-mouth, take my true advice:
Turn around. Go home in a trice.
Give me a better reason
than rowing out from Stafnes this season."

Ólafur didn't bat an eye at the trollwife's words, but he didn't
feel he could take her on in a hostile encounter. So he said:

"Hail to you and hearty greetings,
Hallgerdur of Bláfell."

To which she answered:

"Few addressed me so sweetly of yore,
and go in peace, my dearest dear."

Ólafur followed in the trollwife's tracks and saw a trail of blood
in them. He then offered her a seat on the croup of his packhorse,
provided that she leave it unharmed. She accepted, saying, "Pain's
felt by all, even the troll."
So she rode for a while until she had directed Ólafur on the right
course again. And when they parted, she told him to let his horses
go as soon as he got to the southern parts and not to worry about
them anymore.
Ólafur's journey went smoothly from then on. When he reached
his destination, he let the horses go, and they soon disappeared.
But in the spring, at the end of the fishing season, they returned,
fat and well groomed. Ólafur went back north, and there are no
more stories of him.

Gilitrutt

There was once a young farmer who lived below the mountains
called Eyjafjöll in the South. He was an energetic man and an industrious one. There were good pastures for sheep where he lived, and
he had a large herd. At the time of this story, he was newly married. His wife, though young, was lethargic and lacking in initiative,

too lazy to do almost anything, and took little interest in the household. Although this greatly vexed the young farmer, there was nothing he could do about it.

In the fall after their marriage, he gave her a large quantity of wool and asked her to work it into cloth, but the wife responded with little enthusiasm. By the onset of winter, she hadn't touched the wool, even though her husband often reminded her of it.

One day an old woman of large features came to the farmer's wife and asked her for charity.

"Can you do some work for me in return?" asked the wife.

"That's possible," said the old woman. "What do you want me to do?"

"Work wool into cloth," said the farmer's wife.

"Let me have it, then," answered the old woman.

The farmer's wife picked up an enormous sack of wool and gave it to her. The old woman took it, slung it on her back, and said, "I'll return with the cloth on the first day of summer."

"What do you want in wages?" asked the young wife.

"Not much," said the old one. "You tell me my name on the third guess, and we're even."

The wife agreed to the terms, and the old one left.

As the winter wore on, the farmer often asked his wife where the wool was, but she told him not to worry about it; he would have it on the first day of summer. The farmer was none too happy with the answer but didn't press her any further.

It was now late winter, and the farmer's wife began to ponder over the old woman's name, but she saw no way of finding out, and she became very worried and depressed about it. The husband, seeing how upset she was, asked her to tell him what was wrong. She then told him the whole story. The farmer, frightened, said she had done a stupid thing, for the old woman was no doubt a troll who intended to abduct her.

One day the farmer's business took him into the foothills of the mountains, and he arrived at a large rocky mound. Deep in thought about his troubles, he hardly knew what he was doing. Then he thought he heard a thumping sound coming from inside the mound. Walking toward the sound, he came upon a crack, and through it he saw a woman of large proportions sitting at a loom, which she steadied between her knees while beating the web lustily and chanting to herself:

"Hi hi and ho ho!
The housewife doesn't know my name.
Hi hi and ho ho!
Gilitrutt is my name, ho ho!
Gilitrutt is my name.
Hi hi and ho ho!"

She kept on like that, beating the web with great vigor.

The farmer was now much heartened, for he felt certain that this was the old woman who had come to see his wife in the fall. He went straight home and wrote the name down on a piece of paper: Gilitrutt. He did not, however, tell his wife about it.

The last day of winter arrived, and the wife was so dispirited that she didn't even get out of bed. The farmer came to her, asking if she had found out the name of her "maid." She said no, adding that she would grieve to her death. The farmer told her that would not be necessary, and he gave her the piece of paper with the name on it, informing her how he had found out. She took the note but still trembled with fear that the name might be wrong, and she asked her husband to stay with her when the old one arrived.

"No," he answered. "You took it upon yourself to give her the wool, so it's only fair that you should pay her yourself, too."

With that he left her.

The first day of summer finally came, and the wife lay alone in her bed and no one else in the house. Soon she heard a booming, rumbling noise, and in stepped the old woman, none too pleasant to look at. She flung down a huge roll of cloth, saying, "So, what's my name?"

The farmer's wife, near death from fear, stammered, "Signy?"

"That's my name? That's my name? Guess again, mistress," said the old woman.

"Ása?" said the farmer's wife.

"That's my name? That's my name?" gloated the old one. "Guess once more, mistress!"

"Maybe it's Gilitrutt!" said the farmer's wife.

The old woman had such a shock that she fell headlong on the floor, and what a thunderous noise that made! Then she got up again and left, never to be seen after that.

As for the farmer's wife, she was so grateful to have been delivered from this ogre that she became quite a different person. From

that time on, she was known as an industrious, efficient house-
keeper and always worked her wool herself.

The Night-Troll

It happened at a certain farm that the person who was left to
guard the house on Christmas Eve while the others were at evensong
was always found either dead or mad the following morning.

The farm people were greatly distressed over this, and there
were few who wanted to stay home on that particular night. One
Christmas, however, a young girl volunteered, and that was a relief
to the other members of the household.

After they left, the girl sat on a dais in the *badstofa*, singing to
a baby she held in her arms. As the night wore on, she heard someone at the window, saying:

"What a pretty hand you have,
my quick one, my keen one, and diddly-doe."

The girl answered:

"It has never raked the muck,
my prowler, my Kári, and corry-roe."

The one at the window said:

"What a pretty eye you have,
my quick one, my keen one, and diddly-doe."

And the girl shot back:

"Never has it evil seen,
my prowler, my Kári, and corry-roe."

The answer came from the window:

"What a pretty foot you have,
my quick one, my keen one, and diddly-doe."

To which the girl replied:

"It has never trod in filth,
my prowler, my Kári, and corry-roe."

From the voice at the window came:

"Day is dawning in the east,
my quick one, my keen one, and diddly-doe."

And the girl within retorted:

"Stay and turn to stone,
but be of harm to no one,
my prowler, my Kári, and corry-roe."

Then the being disappeared from the window.

In the morning, when the farm people returned, a huge boulder was found in the alley between the farmhouses, and it has remained there ever since.

The girl recounted everything that had happened during the night. It appeared that it had been a night-troll that spoke to her through the window.

"Deep Indeed the Iceland Channels"

Legend has it that a certain trollwife wanted to wade over to Iceland from Norway. She was aware that there were some channels on the way, for she is said to have remarked to another trollwife, a neighbor who wanted to deter her, "They're deep indeed the Iceland channels, and yet they are fordable." Nevertheless, she mused, there was one narrow trench near the middle of the ocean so deep that her head might get wet in it.

After that she set off wading and reached the channel of which she was most wary. Then a ship went sailing by, and she wanted to grab it and use it for support across. But she missed it by an inch and stumbled at the same time, falling headlong into the trench where she drowned. Her body later washed ashore at Raudisandur in the West. It was so huge that a man on horseback couldn't even reach with his whip handle into the ham of her bent knee, where she lay dead and stiff on the foreshore.

Ghosts and Sorcerers

"Mother in the Pen, Pen"

There once was a maid at a farm. She had become pregnant, given birth, and exposed her child to die — which was not all that rare in Iceland, even when such a deed called for harsh penance, fines, or death.

Some time after this happened, a dance of the kind called *vikivaki*, formerly quite common in the country, was to be held, and this same girl was invited to it. But because she loved pretty clothes, yet had no garments fine enough for such a gathering, she became very distressed, thinking she would have to stay home and miss the dance.

One evening, shortly before the dance, the maid was milking ewes in the sheep pen along with another woman. Then she began complaining to her companion that she had nothing to wear for the *vikivaki*. As soon as she had spoken, they heard a verse chanted under the wall of the pen:

> Mother in the pen, pen,
> primp and charm the men, men.
> Take my swaddling rags to don
> and dance in them,
> and dance in them.

Thinking that she detected in it a barb meant for her, the girl who had exposed her child to die was startled out of her wits by the verse, and she remained that way for the rest of her life.

"Give Me Back My Bone, Gunna"

It was customary for people in the countryside to take light with them to the cowshed in the winter. Usually, the source of light used on such occasions was a simple lamp called *kola* (or pan). It was a thin, shallow kind of vessel with a narrow handle sticking out of it, which would fit into a hole in any vertical post in the shed to illuminate the place while people were working there. The *kola* had a lighted wick and fish or train oil to feed it and was generally carried to the shed, already lit, in a protective covering that was specifically made for the purpose and called a light carrier. It was shaped like a gabled house with a sharp-angled roof. A small opening was left next to the bottom at one end of the light carrier, through which the *kola* could be slid inside it to be carried to the cowshed.

One winter, a girl named Gudrún, who was a dairymaid at a parsonage, having lost or broken her *kola*, resolved to take a shard of human skull that had been dug up in the graveyard, light a wick in it, and use it for a lamp. This was of little consequence through the early part of winter and past Christmas. But on New Year's Eve, when the girl had carried her light to the cowshed as usual, she heard a voice calling her through the window, saying, "Give me back my bone, Gunna!"

Gudrún made short shrift of it, took the piece of skull as it was, light and all, flung it in the manure trough, stomped on it, and said, "Then come and get it, damn you!"

Another version has it that Gudrún only flung the piece of skull in the direction from which the sound had come but didn't stomp on it. However it was, the girl suffered no harm.

"Gone Is My Glowing Skin Tone"

Once, at a pastorage, a dead person had to be buried, and the pastor's hired hands were set to dig the grave. Also in the pastor's household was a spunky young servant girl. When the grave was almost ready, she happened to walk through the churchyard, and just as she was going by, the grave-diggers turned up a human bone; it was a thigh-bone of enormous size.

The girl caught sight of the bone and picked it up. As she was examining it, she remarked, "It would have been fun to kiss him when he was alive."

Then she put the bone down and walked off.

The day passed into evening. When it was dark and the lamps had been lit, the pastor found he needed a book that he had left on the altar of the church earlier in the day. He asked the girl to go and get it for him, for she had a reputation of being totally unafraid of the dark.

The girl had no objection.

So she went out to the church, picked up the book from the altar, and returned back down the aisle. When she reached the door, she saw a man of huge stature sitting in the last pew on the north side. He addressed her, speaking this verse:

> "Gone is my glowing skin tone,
> good my maid, and faded.
> Look in my dead eyes, lady,
> lustrous of old, though cold now.
> Hacked in half my buckler
> had I of yore in war; my
> beard's uncleaned, but kindly
> kiss me if you still wish to."

The girl, not the least taken aback, went over to the man and kissed him. Then she returned to the house with the book and thought nothing of it.

Another version of the story has it that the girl didn't dare kiss the man when he challenged her but ran in panic out of the church and never was the same again. All agree, however, that the thigh-bone uncovered in the grave must have been that of some gigantic saga-age warrior, the very one who sat in the pew and spoke the verse.

The Ghost and the Cash Box

There was once a steward of a church farm in northern Iceland. He was a married man of great wealth, much concerned with hoarding money, and it was known for certain that he had a large amount of cash. The man was closefisted, while his wife was kind and charitable, but she had no influence over her husband.

One winter the steward became ill. He died soon after, and his body was laid out and buried. After that, his estate was settled, but it was found to include no money. The widow was asked if she knew anything about her husband's money, but she said she didn't know of a single penny, and since she was known to be an honest sort, her word was not questioned. People surmised that the steward had buried his money — which later proved to be the case.

As the winter wore on, people began to be aware of hauntings at the farm and felt sure that it was the steward who had returned to be near his money. The situation grew worse as time passed, and in the spring most of the hired people were prepared to leave the widow. She, in turn, was ready to give up the farm.

So it went until Moving Days. At that time a field hand came to the widow offering his services, and she took him on. Having been there a short while, however, he discovered that the farm was badly haunted, and at one time he asked the widow if her husband had had a lot of money. She replied she knew nothing about it.

Summer now passed into fall, and it was market time. Then the field hand went to town, and among other things he bought was a quantity of tin sheets and white linen. When he returned, he had a shroud sewn from the linen, while he himself — being a skilled metal worker — began to fashion himself gloves out of the tin sheets.

One evening, when the nights had grown dark again and everybody had gone to sleep, the field hand put on his tin gloves, placed a sheet of the metal on his chest, and donned the shroud to cover it all. Then he went out into the churchyard, close to the steward's grave, and paced back and forth, playing with a silver piece in the palm of his hand.

Not long afterward a ghost rose out of the steward's grave. He was quick to spot the field hand.

"Are you one of us?" he asked.

"Yes," said the hired man.

"Let me feel," said the ghost.

The field worker gave him his hand, and the ghost felt it was cold.

"Yes, you're a ghost all right," he said. "What did you return for?"

"To play with my silver piece," said the field hand.

"Poor wretch!" exclaimed the ghost. "What if you had as much money as I do?"

"You have a lot of money?" asked the hired man.

"Yessir!" replied the ghost, and with that he ran out of the churchyard, the hired man following. They went on until they were close to the edge of the homefield. Here the ghost kicked over a hummock and pulled his cash box out of the earth. The two of them then began to play with the money and spent most of the night at it. When it was drawing near dawn, the ghost wanted to gather up the money and put it away, but the hired man said he hadn't seen the small coins yet and scattered them all over again. The ghost looked at him and said, "You can't be a ghost."

"Sure I am," said the hired man. "Just feel for yourself." And he held out his other hand.

"It's true," said the ghost, and again he began to gather up his coins while the hired man continued to fling them all over the place.

The ghost now got good and mad, saying the other must be alive and wanted to betray him. The hired man denied this again. Then the ghost grabbed him by the chest, but feeling it was cold had to admit, "It's true what you say. You're the same as I."

Once more the ghost began gathering up his money, and this time the hired man no longer dared prevent it.

"I'm going to put my silver piece in with your money," he said.

"Sure, why don't you," said the ghost. He put the hummock back in place so no one could see it had been disturbed, and the two of them returned to the churchyard.

"Where is your hole?" asked the ghost when they were there.

"It's on the other side of the church," said the other.

"You go in first," said the ghost.

"No," said the hired man. "You go first."

There they stood arguing about it until day broke and the ghost had to jump into his grave. The hired man went into the farmhouse, filled a tun with water, placed it under the landing, and put his outfit from the night in it. He also went out and got the cash box, which he put into the tun as well.

The day passed until evening, and everybody went to bed. The hired man slept opposite the door, and the night wasn't old when the ghost entered, sniffing in all directions but finding nothing. Angered, he struck his fist against the edge of the landing — and a mighty blow it was — before he went out again. The hired man followed him, and the story goes that he then fixed the steward's grave so that his ghost was never seen after that. The reason the hired man put his outfit and the cash box into the tun was that he wouldn't have the ghost smell the earth on them.

The hired man later married the widow, and they lived together a long time.

And that's the end of this tale.

The Deacon of Myrká

In former days there was a deacon at the church of Myrká in Eyjafjördur. His name has not been recorded, but he was having a love affair with a woman named Gudrún, who is said to have lived at Baegisá on the other side of the river Hörgá, apparently a maid to the pastor there. The deacon had a gray-maned horse called Faxi, which he always rode.

One day, shortly before Christmas, the deacon went over to Baegisá to invite Gudrún to the Christmas dance at Myrká, and he promised he would come for her at a certain hour on Christmas Eve to escort her to the dance. For some days before the deacon went to invite Gudrún, there had been heavy snowfall and freezing cold, but the day he rode over to Baegisá there was a sudden thaw so the ice melted and broke. And as the day wore on and the deacon tarried at Baegisá, the river became impassable because of ice-drift and swelling flood waters. When he left for home, the deacon was unaware of what had happened during the day, and he took it for granted that the river was still frozen as before. He managed to cross the Yxnadalsá by an ice-bridge, but when he reached the Hörgá, it had cleared itself of ice, so he rode down along the river until he came to a spot opposite Saurbaer, the next farm downstream from Myrká. There he found an ice-bridge still intact. The deacon rode out on the bridge, but when he was half-way across, it broke under him, and he fell into the river.

The morning after, when the farmer of Thúfnavellir got up, he saw a saddled horse below his homefield and thought he recognized the deacon's Faxi. This gave him a jolt, for he had seen the deacon go by the day before but hadn't noticed him return, and he soon suspected what had happened. He went down across his homefield and found his hunch confirmed, for it was indeed Faxi, all wet and badly bruised. Seeing that, he continued all the way to the river and out to the so-called Thúfnavallanes, where he discovered the deacon washed up dead. The farmer lost no time going to Myrká to tell the news. When he was found, the deacon had a deep gash at the back of his head, apparently made by an ice-floe. His body was taken to Myrká and buried there in the week before Christmas.

From the time the deacon left Baegisá until Christmas Eve, no word had passed about this event between Myrká and Baegisá owing to the thaw and the swollen waters. But on Christmas Eve the weather was much better, and the flood had abated during the night. Gudrún therefore was looking forward to the dance at Myrká. She began to dress in the late afternoon, and when she was almost ready, she heard a knock on the door. Another woman who was there with her went to the door but saw no one outside, perhaps because it was neither light nor dark. The moon was riding in clouds, alternately hiding behind them and peeping through. When the girl returned inside saying she hadn't seen anyone, Gudrún replied, "I guess it's a game played for my benefit, so I'll go out."

By that time she was fully dressed, except for her overcoat. She took the coat and slipped her arm through one sleeve, but threw the other over her shoulder and held it that way.

When she got outside, she saw Faxi standing by the door and beside the horse a man whom she took to be the deacon. It is not known if they spoke to each other at that time, but the man lifted Gudrún onto the horse and seated himself in front of her. They rode like that for a while without speaking. When they reached the Hörgá, the ice-banks were quite high, and as the horse went over the edge, the deacon's hat was lifted at the back, and Gudrún looked at his bare skull. At that very moment the clouds cleared from the moon, and the deacon said:

"The moon is gliding.
Death is riding.
Don't you see a white spot
at the nape of my neck
Garún, Garún?"

She was startled but remained silent. (Some people say that Gudrún herself lifted the deacon's hat at the back and having seen the white skull, said, "I see how it is.") Nothing else has been told of their conversation or their journey until they came to Myrká, where they dismounted in front of the lychgate. Then the deacon said to Gudrún:

"Wait here for me, Garún, Garún,
while I take my Faxi, Faxi,
over to the pasture, pasture."

So saying, he went off with the horse, while Gudrún, looking about, happened to glance into the churchyard. There she saw an open grave and became very frightened, yet she had sense enough to grab the bell rope. At that precise moment she was clutched from

51

behind, and it was her good luck that she hadn't had time to put her arms through both coat sleeves, for so powerful was the jerk that the coat tore at the shoulder on the sleeve she was wearing. The last she saw of the deacon was that he plunged headlong into the open grave, the tattered coat in his hands, and the earth rushed in over him as if swept from both sides.

As for Gudrún, she kept ringing the bell until the farm people came out and took her inside. She had become so terrified that she dared neither move from the spot nor stop ringing, for even though she had had no word of the deacon's death, she felt sure she had been dealing with his ghost. This was confirmed to her when she spoke to the Myrká people, who told her of the deacon's death while she in turn recounted her journey.

That same night, when everyone was in bed and the lights were out, the deacon came to haunt Gudrún, and so persistent was he that the people had to get up again, and no one could sleep that night. For a fortnight after that, Gudrún could never be alone and had to be watched over every night. Some say the pastor had to sit on the edge of her bed and read from the Psalter.

At that point a wizard was sent for to Skagafjördur. When he arrived, he had a great big rock unearthed above the hayfield and rolled home to the gable of the house. In the evening, as it was getting dark, the deacon appeared and tried to get into the house, but the wizard drove him out to the gable end and buried him there with some powerful incantations. Then he rolled the rock over to the spot, and there the deacon is supposed to rest to this very day.

After this, all the hauntings ceased at Myrká, and Gudrún began to recover. She returned home to Baegisá shortly afterward, but it is said she was never quite the same again.

The Wizards of the Westman Islands

When the Black Death was ravaging Iceland, eighteen wizards gathered together and formed a partnership. They went out to the Westman Islands, their intent to ward off death as long as they could. When they had signs that the epidemic was beginning to abate on the mainland, they wanted to know if anyone had been left alive. Agreeing to send one of their own over to investigate, they chose a fellow whose skill in their art was neither the greatest nor the least but just about average. They took him ashore and told him that if he hadn't returned by Christmas, they would dispatch a *sending* that would kill him.

This was in early Advent.

The man set off and walked for a long time, ranging far and wide, but nowhere did he see a single person alive. The farmhouses stood open, and dead bodies lay scattered about them. Finally, however, he came to a farm where the door was shut. This was a surprise, and he began to entertain the hope that he might find someone alive. He knocked on the door, and a young, pretty girl came out. As he greeted her, she flung her arms around his neck, crying with joy over seeing another human being, for she had thought that she was the only survivor. She asked the wizard to stay with her, to which he agreed, and they went inside and had a long talk. She inquired where he came from and where he was going. Having told her that, he added that he had to go back before Christmas. But when she pleaded with him to stay as long as possible, he took pity on her and made her the promise. She informed him that nobody was alive in the surrounding area, for she had traveled a week in all directions and found no one.

Time passed, and Christmas approached. Then the islander wanted to go. But the girl beseeched him to stay, arguing that his companions couldn't be so cruel as to punish him for remaining with her, a poor orphan. He gave in.

Christmas Eve arrived, and the man resolved to go no matter what the girl said. Then, seeing that prayers would no longer avail her, she changed her tune, saying, "Do you really think you can reach the islands tonight? Don't you think it's as good to die here with me as somewhere on the way?" The man realized that he had run out of time and that he had best stay and await his death right there.

The night wore on. The man was very dispirited, but the girl was as cheerful as could be, asking if he had any idea how the islanders were getting on. He replied that they had already dispatched the *sending* to the mainland and it would arrive that same day. The girl sat down on her bed with him, and he lay on the other side of it, up against the wall. Remarking that he was getting drowsy — a fact that he attributed to the effect of the *sending* — he soon fell asleep. The girl remained sitting on the edge of the bed and kept rousing him from time to time so he could tell her how the *sending* was proceeding. But the nearer it drew, the deeper his sleep became. Finally, having declared that the *sending* was now within the boundaries of the farm, he fell so fast asleep that the girl could no longer wake him. At the same time she noticed that a rust-colored cloud of vapor was seeping into the house.

This vapor approached her very slowly and assumed a human shape. The girl asked where, pray, it thought it was going, and the *sending* told her all about its mission, finally asking her to get off the bed, "for I can't get past you," it said.

The girl answered that it would have to earn her cooperation, and the *sending* asked how. By showing her how big it could get, said the girl. The *sending* agreed and made itself so large that it filled the entire house.

Then the girl said, "Now I want to see how small you can make yourself."

The *sending* told her it could turn into a fly and immediately assumed such a shape, intending to sneak under the girl's arm and thus get at the man in the bed. But instead it flew right into a hollow sheep's leg the girl was holding and which she now promptly plugged. After that she put the leg-bone, *sending* and all, in her pocket and roused her companion.

The man woke up quickly and could hardly believe he was still alive. The girl asked him where the *sending* was now, and he said he had no idea what had become of it. That, said the girl, just confirmed her long-standing suspicion that those island chaps weren't the wizards they were made out to be. The man was very glad, and they both thoroughly enjoyed their Christmas.

As New Year drew near, however, the man again grew silent. The girl asked what was bothering him. He replied that the islanders were preparing another *sending*, "and they're all putting their spells together to make it more powerful. It'll be here on New Year's Eve, and there won't be any escape for me."

The girl said she wouldn't worry about that so soon, "and don't be afraid of those *sendings* from the islanders," she said. She remained so cheerful that he was ashamed to show any signs of fear.

On New Year's Eve the man said the *sending* had reached the mainland. "And it's moving very quickly," he said, "for it's extremely powerful."

The girl told him to come outside with her, and so he did. They walked until they came to a thicket. There the girl stopped, removed a few twigs, and uncovered a slab of stone. She lifted the slab, and underneath it gaped the entrance to a subterranean chamber.

The two of them descended into the chamber, which was dark and terrifying. One dim lamp was there, made out of a human skull and burning the belly-fat of a man. On an earthen bunk next to the light lay an old codger rather scary to look at. His eyes were all bloodshot and his face so unsightly that it frightened the islander.

"Something must be wrong, my child, that you should come here," said the old one. "It's a long time since I've seen you. What can I do for you?"

The girl told him all that had come to pass and about the man and the first *sending*. The old man asked to see the leg-bone, and the girl gave it to him. With the bone in his hands, the old fellow looked like a different man. He turned the bone this way and that way, looking at it from every possible angle, and fondled it in his hands.

Then the girl pleaded, "Help me now, fosterfather, and hurry, for the man is beginning to get drowsy, and that means the *sending* will soon be here."

The old man then unplugged the leg-bone, and the fly came crawling out of it. The old man caressed and patted the fly, saying, "Now go meet all the *sendings* from the islands and swallow them up!"

No sooner had he uttered the words than there was a great big crash, and the fly buzzed off, growing so enormous that one jaw brushed the sky while the other swept the ground. In this way it countered all the *sendings* from the islands, and the man was saved.

After that the pair of them returned to the girl's farm, and there they settled down and married and multiplied and filled the earth.

Rusty of Írafell

There was a man named Kort Thorvardsson, a member of the parish council and a farmer of substance. He lived for a long time at Mödruvellir in the Kjós district but finally moved to Flekkudalur, where he died in 1821.

Kort was twice married. His first wife was named Ingibjörg and the second Thórdís Jónsdóttir. Ingibjörg hailed from the North. She had had many suitors before she met Kort but had refused them all. Even though Kort was their better in most ways, these previous admirers felt abused when he was successful where they had not been, and they became so vengeful that they paid a northern sorcerer to dispatch a *sending* against Kort and his wife. The sorcerer's choice was a little boy who is said to have died of exposure. Raising him while he was still warm, or not yet quite dead, the sorcerer sent him to the newly-weds at Mödruvellir with the stipulation that he follow them and their descendants through the ninth generation and do them much harm.

Those who saw Rusty — and there were many of them — described him as wearing gray breeches and a rust-colored coat, and on his head he had a black, wide-brimmed hat with a deep notch or gap in the brim over his left eye. He was named for his coat and therefore called Rusty. The sorcerer's stipulation was fulfilled all too well, for when Rusty arrived in the South, he put up at Mödruvellir, as intended, and did the couple countless injuries of many sorts, not only by killing their livestock but also by spoiling their food. No instance was related, however, that Rusty ever killed people directly.

At one time, Kort and his wife had reared two calves over the winter. The following summer, Rusty chased both of them over a cliff; they were found dead at the foot of the precipice. Another time, Kort had a mare that summer-long grazed with her foal in the home pasture at Mödruvellir. Late in the summer the foal was seen running madly around a rock and then falling. On examination, it was found dead; somehow, it had got its end-gut stuck on the rock and had pulled out its own intestines until it fell dead. This was blamed on Rusty.

Because Rusty was supposed to have been not quite dead when he was raised, he had to have his full share of food like all ghosts of that sort. Consequently, he had to be given his portion like any other person in the household. This was true both at Mödruvellir and at Írafell after he lodged himself there to harass Kort's son, Magnús. The food intended for him was always put in a secluded place. Rusty had achieved this by completely spoiling everything in Ingibjörg's larder at Mödruvellir. Sometimes he would sit on the cross-beams and splash in the milk troughs with his feet, or else turn them over; and he would throw *skyr* both at her and all about the larder, from rafters to floor, or fling turf and stones into the food wherever it was and spoil it that way. Because of this, Ingibjörg resolved to apportion him a full meal twice a day, after which he pretty much stopped spoiling the food. Once, however, it happened that Rusty's evening meal was forgotten. The following morning he was found in the larder, straddling the rims of two tuns of *skyr*, one foot inside each, at once busily churning the *skyr* with his feet and flinging it about with his hands. After that, great care was taken not to forget his meals.

— Food, however, wasn't all Rusty needed; he also had to rest like anybody else. So, after he attached himself to Magnús Kortsson at Írafell, the story goes that an empty bed always had to be left for him opposite Magnús's own, and no one had better lie in it but Rusty alone.

One day at round-up time, many people had gathered at Írafell to stay overnight. Later in the evening a boy arrived and asked to be put up, too. Magnús told him he was welcome to stay but said he had no place for him to sleep except the floor, unless he wanted to lie in the bed opposite his own, which the boy gratefully accepted. When he lay down to rest that night, the boy fell asleep soon enough, but barely had he done so when something weighed on him so dreadfully that it made his throat rattle. He woke up with a start, and for the rest of the night he couldn't sleep a wink because of similar attacks.

The following day the weather was so bad that the guests couldn't leave, and they stayed over another night at Írafell. That evening some boys who lived at the farm and knew Rusty, having frequently engaged him in mudslinging, got together and placed numerous knives, points up, all around the bed. That night the visiting boy slept soundly, and it was attributed to the fact that Rusty hadn't dared come near him for fear of the knives.

After Kort's death in 1821, Rusty at first followed his eldest son, Magnús. As previously mentioned, Magnús farmed at Írafell most of his life, and it was because Rusty stayed there so long that he became known as Rusty of Írafell.

It is said that once, in a good fishing year, Magnús went down to Seltjarnarnes, but since he had secured no permanent place on any boat, he went from one to another, being allowed a place here and there on a daily basis. On two consecutive days he got a boat space with farmer Sigurdur of Hrólfsskáli. But on the second day, Sigurdur's crew began to notice that Magnús, wherever he happened to be, was never alone. The third morning, when Magnús had boarded and Sigurdur's boat was already afloat, the crew spoke up about Rusty. According to the story, they had seen something akin to a rust-colored clew of yarn or a piece of horse dung roll aboard the boat along with Magnús. Hearing this, Sigurdur, who was considered a cautious, intelligent man, ordered Magnús off the boat and refused to carry him any longer, either because he himself had become aware of Rusty, or he didn't want his crew to look askance at Magnús and blame him for bringing them bad luck should anything go wrong.

At one time, Magnús of Írafell had left a copy of Hallgrímur Pétursson's *Passion Hymns* with farmer Ásgeir Finnbogason of Brádraedi, who was supposed to bind it for him. One night, Ásgeir was not at home, and his wife waited up for him. At first she kept herself busy doing some chores but later went to bed, waiting there by light until Ásgeir returned home. Then he, too, went to bed, and they put out the light. Right afterward, she saw a boy enter the room, sit down on a chair beside the bed, and put his arm in over the bedboard. She happened to be sleeping on the outer side of the bed, and she found the arm so heavy and oppressive that she called out asking if it was Jóhannes, their fosterson. But there was no answer. She repeated the question and then told the visitor, whosoever he was, to go to hell. Then the one sitting on the chair stood up, opened his eyes up wide so they glinted in the moonlight shining in through the window, and dashed out — through the locked door. A thunderous crash followed, and at the same moment a shelf on the other side of the room, diagonally opposite the bed, fell down. The shelf had held many books, among them the copy of the *Passion Hymns* that Ásgeir had taken from Magnús to bind. In addition, the shelf had held several pieces of china, which, as was to be expected, were smashed to tiny shards that flew all over the floor. Mistress Sigrídur then relit the lamp and had someone sit up with her the rest of the night; she got little sleep. In the early hours next morning, Magnús came to Brádraedi asking for the book that had been on the shelf, and he was informed what a pleasant companion he had.

Rusty also attached himself to Magnús' only son, Gudmundur. One winter, farmer Ásgeir, now living at Lambastadir near Reykjavík, sent his son, named Thorvaldur, to be tutored by the pastor of Reynivellir in the Kjós district. The boy returned home shortly before Christmas in order to spend the holidays with his parents, and it was agreed that he would be accompanied back to Reynivellir after Christmas, when someone from the Kjós district would be traveling to Reykjavík.

One night at Lambastadir, Thorvaldur and his mother were sleeping by themselves in the *badstofa*; it was late, and the lights were out. Suddenly, the boy's mother felt ill and asked him to relight the lamp. When he had done so, she asked him to get her a drink of water and to take the lamp with him so he wouldn't bump into anything. Thorvaldur was only twelve at the time, but he was unafraid of the dark and felt he didn't need the lamp. So, when he went for the water, he left the light in the *badstofa* but kept the door open so the glow from it would be thrown into the kitchen.

When Thorvaldur turned around, having filled a glass with water, he saw a small boy step from the foyer and onto the kitchen floor; the doors had not been locked in the evening. The boy planted himself there in the glow of the light, his head bare but a wide-brimmed hat in his hand, and wearing a rust-colored coat. He stared at Thorvaldur with his big eyes, a roguish grin on his face, and for a while they gazed at each other that way. Thorvaldur said afterward that he had not been afraid of him but observed him closely, and he recalled that the boy had seemed all hairy in the face. It was only when Thorvaldur turned away that he gave a start so the water splashed from the glass, for at that moment a dog that had been lying in the *badstofa* jumped up with a ferocious bark and dashed through the kitchen and out into the homefield; other dogs joined in, and they kept barking for a long time.

The next day two men from the Kjós district came for Thorvaldur, and one of them happened to be Gudmundur Magnússon. It was then concluded that it must have been Rusty of Írafell that Thorvaldur had seen the previous night.

Tales of Saemundur the Learned

1. The Black School

In olden times there was a school over the seas called the Black School, where young men studied sorcery and all kinds of ancient lore. This school was housed in an underground bunker, very sturdily built; it had no windows, so it was pitch-dark inside. Nor was there any teacher; everything the students learned, they got from books written in fiery red letters which could be read in the dark. Those who enrolled were forbidden to go out in the open air or see the light of day while attending the school, and to complete their studies, they had to remain there for three or seven years. A gray, hairy hand would come through the wall every day delivering meals to the students. The master of the school reserved the right to keep the one graduate each year who was the last to leave. And since it was common knowledge that the master was the Devil himself, everyone wanted to avoid being the last to exit.

Once there were three Icelanders together at the Black School: Saemundur the Learned, Kálfur Árnason, and Hálfdan Eldjárnsson or Einarsson, later priest at Fell in Slétuhlíd. They were all graduating at the same time, and Saemundur offered to be the last one out. That was a great relief to the others. Saemundur then wrapped himself in a large overcoat but let the sleeves hang empty and did not button the coat.

A flight of stairs led out of the schoolhouse. As Saemundur was walking up the stairs, the Devil grabbed him by the coat and said, "You're mine!" Saemundur then let loose the coat and ran out, leaving Old Nick with the garment alone in his hands. The iron door creaked and rumbled on its hinges and banged shut so tightly behind Saemundur that his heel bones were hurt. "A close call," he remarked — which has since been a popular phrase. In this way, Saemundur got away from the Black School along with his companions.

Another version has it that when Saemundur walked up the stairs and reached the door of the Black School, the sun shone in, casting his shadow on the inside wall. And when the Devil attempted to seize Saemundur, he said, "I'm not the last one. Don't you see the one behind me?"

The Devil reached out for the shadow, thinking it was a man, while Saemundur got out and the door slammed shut on his heels. But from that time on, he was a man without a shadow, for the Devil never let go of it.

2. How Saemundur Got His Benefice

When Saemundur, Kálfur, and Hálfdan left the Black School, the benefice of Oddi was vacant, and they all applied to the king for it. The king knew full well with whom he was dealing and told them that whoever could get there first would have the Oddi.

Saemundur immediately went to summon Old Nick, saying, "Swim with me on your back out to Iceland, and if you can get me ashore without wetting my coattails, my soul is yours."

Old Nick agreed to this, quickly changed into a seal, and set off with Saemundur on his back. On the way, Saemundur continuously read in his Psalter. In a short time they were close to land in Iceland. Then Saemundur struck the seal over the head with the Psalter so the creature sank; Saemundur was temporarily submerged but swam ashore.

And that's how the Devil lost his bargain and Saemundur got the Oddi.

3. Gathering the Hay

Saemundur the Learned once had a considerable quantity of dry hay in the field while the outlook was for rain. So he asked all his working people to pull together and try to save the hay.

At that time, there was one very old woman in his household at Oddi, and Saemundur went to her, too, asking if she would try to limp out to the field and rake together whatever scattered remnants of hay the others left. She said she would. Then she took her rake, tying onto the end of it the bonnet off her head, and shuffled out to the field. To Saemundur, she said he had better stay in the yard and stack the hay, for his field hands wouldn't take long binding it and bringing it home.

The cleric said he would do just that; it would be for the best.

The old one stuck the end of her rake under each of the bundles of hay, saying, "Up to the yard to Saemundur with you!" and the bundles went there straightaway. Saemundur then told Old Nick and his imps to make haste. And in a short time, all the hay was home in the yard, safe from the rain.

Afterward, Saemundur said to the crone, "I guess you know a thing or two, my dear old Thórhildur."

"It isn't much now," she replied. "I've forgotten most of what I knew in my younger days."

4. The Imp Whistle

Saemundur the Learned had a whistle possessed of a very peculiar quality: Whenever it was blown, one or more imps would appear, asking what they should do.

One day, Saemundur left the whistle under the pillow in his

bed, where he always kept it at night. In the evening he told his maid to prepare his bed as usual but warned her that if she came across anything out of the ordinary, she should not touch it but just leave it be.

The girl began to prepare the bed, and when she saw the whistle, she couldn't check her curiosity. She picked it up at once, examined it closely, and finally blew it. An imp immediately appeared to her, asking, "What do you wish me to do?"

The girl was startled, but she acted unperturbed. It so happened that ten of Saemundur's wethers had been slaughtered earlier in the day, and all the skins were lying about outside. The girl told the imp that he should count every hair on all the skins, and if he could finish before she had made the bed, he could have her.

The imp went out and began counting, while the girl hastened to make the bed. When she had finished, the imp still had one more skin to go, so he lost out on the bargain. Saemundur later asked the girl if she had found anything in his bed. She told him the truth, and Saemundur was quite pleased with her presence of mind.

5. The Imp and the Cowherd

Saemundur the Learned once had a cowherd who he felt swore far too much, and he often admonished him about it. He told the cowherd that the Devil and all his imps fed on the oaths and bad language people used.

"Well," said the cowherd, "if I knew that Old Nick would starve because of it, I would never utter a wicked word."

"We'll soon see how serious you are," said Saemundur, and he placed an imp in the cowbarn.

The cowherd detested his new boarder because the imp did everything he could to harm and irk him, and it was just barely that the poor fellow could keep from cursing. Yet some time passed during which he was very nearly successful, and he noticed that the imp grew thinner every day. This pleased the cowherd very much, and he soon stopped swearing altogether.

Then one morning he came to the cowbarn to find it in total shambles and the cows all tied together by their tails — and there were quite a few of them. Seeing this, the cowherd turned on the imp, who was lying there in his stall half-dead with misery, and poured out his fury with dreadful oaths and ugly curses. To his distress, however, the imp suddenly began to revive and in no time became so plump and portly as to verge on obesity. Then the cowherd controlled himself and stopped cursing. The truth of the Reverend Saemundur's words had been driven home to him, and he never swore or uttered a bad word after that. As for the imp who was supposed to feed on his profanities — well, he soon went the way of all flesh.

You and I had better follow the cowherd's example.

6. Old Nick's Pact With the Weaver

With Saemundur the Learned at Oddi, there once was a maid who wove most of the fabric needed in the household. One day as she was at the loom, a man came to her and struck up a conversation. He asked if being in service at Oddi wasn't pretty bad. She said it wasn't too bad, although once in a while the food was rather skimpy because so much went to feed visitors and wayfarers.

"You go hungry once in a while, then?" the man asked.

"Not as a rule," replied the maid.

"Wouldn't it be good, though, if you found a buttered cake each evening by your bedside?"

She said she wouldn't mind.

He told her he would see to it that cake and butter be at her bedside every evening, but she would have to promise him in return never to pray for Saemundur, for if she did, she wouldn't get the cake and butter.

She said she would do as he asked.

For a long time that winter, she never prayed for Saemundur. Even when he sneezed and all the other people present bid God bless him, she never did. Consequently, there was always a buttered cake at her bedside every evening.

Once as she was weaving, Saemundur came by and began talking to her. And when he had done so for a spell, he had a severe sneezing fit. She kept silent, acting as if she'd heard nothing. After some time, he started sneezing still more vehemently. Then the poor girl couldn't stand it anymore, and she said, "Don't sneeze your sense away, Reverend Saemundur. God help you."

The Reverend Saemundur immediately stopped sneezing and said, "I don't think you'll have your cake and butter tonight."

And from then on she never got cake and butter from Old Nick again.

Tales of the Reverend Eiríkur of Vogsósar

Numerous tales are told of the Reverend Eiríkur of Vogsósar, the best ones coming from his home district of Selvogur in the Southwest. According to those who knew, Eiríkur was "eccentric and learned in magic, frequently entered hills, and did many other strange things. He never harmed anybody with his knowledge but was not above playing practical jokes, especially if provoked. It was Eiríkur's custom to disappear from his parsonage every Saturday night, not to return again until Sunday morning. No one ever knew what he was doing during these absences of his."

1. How Eiríkur Learned Magic in School

In the district of Biskupstungur, in the South, there once was an old, eccentric cotter who didn't much mix with other folks. Two things in his possession he valued more than anything else: a book whose contents no one knew and a heifer which he fed prodigiously. The cotter contracted a severe illness and sent word to the bishop of Skálholt, asking him to come and see him. The bishop, thinking he might persuade the old man to repent his sins, reacted quickly and went to his bedside.

"It so happens, sir," said the cotter, "that I am about to die, and I want to ask a small favor."

The bishop said he would listen.

"I have here a book," continued the old one, "and a heifer I am very fond of, and I want both to be buried with me, or else there will be consequences."

The bishop promised this would be done, for he was afraid the cotter would otherwise return to haunt him. Then the old man died, and the bishop had him buried with the book and the heifer.

A long time after this happened, three youths at the school of Skálholt began to study black magic. One of them was named Bogi, another Magnús, and the third Eiríkur. They had been told of the old cotter and his book, and they wanted very much to get hold of it, so they proceeded one night to raise the old man out of his grave. The trouble was that no one knew exactly where the grave was. They finally resorted to calling up all the dead, row by row, and filled the church with ghosts, but the cotter wasn't among them. Putting these to rest again, they filled the church the second and third time, at which point only a few graves remained, but the cotter still wasn't there. When they had put all these into the ground again, they conjured up those who were left, and finally the old cotter appeared, the very last, holding the book under his arm and leading the heifer.

The three young men all set on the old one at once, trying to get at the book. But the cotter reacted vehemently, so they had their hands full just defending themselves. Nevertheless, they managed to tear off a part from the front of the book, and that in hand, they decided to abandon the fight for the remainder and put all the ghosts back to rest. They succeeded in doing this — that is, with all except the old cotter. Desperately seeking to regain his book, he would not be controlled. But the youths held him off, which was all they could do, until dawn. As day broke, the cotter returned to his grave, they recited their formulas over it, and the old man has never since made his presence felt. The three comrades used the pages they acquired to compose a book of magic named *Grayskin*, which was long kept on the classroom table at Skálholt. Its chief author was Bogi, for he was by far the most advanced of them.

All three of them were ordained as ministers. Eiríkur became the parson at Vogsósar in Selvogur, but the others' benefices have not been identified. It is said, however, that Magnús wooed and married Bogi's fiancée, and when the latter learned of it, he set off to see Magnús. But Magnús knew he was on the way, and he also knew that if Bogi set eyes on him first, it would be his death. So, Magnús went to his church, where he hid behind the door, and instructed his servants to tell Bogi, upon arrival, that he was at the altar saying his prayers. Bogi went to the church and stepped into the middle of the aisle where Magnús saw him first and bid him welcome. Bogi responded with good cheer, and when he left again, Magnús saw him off. In parting, Bogi took a flask out of his pocket, offering Magnús a sip. Taking the flask, Magnús uncorked it and threw the contents in Bogi's face, who instantly fell down dead. Magnús thereupon returned home, and nothing more is said of him.

When Eiríkur of Vogsósar learned of all this, he was startled and said, "Ah yes, my pet," which was his customary address, "we were all children compared with Bogi."

Although the companions had tried to hide their learning in magic, the rumor soon spread that Eiríkur of Vogsósar was a sorcerer. The bishop therefore summoned him to a meeting, showed him the *Grayskin* volume, and asked him to state if he knew its teaching. Eiríkur leafed through the book and said, "I don't know *one* letter in it." On this he took an oath and then returned home. To an acquaintance of his he later explained that he knew every letter of it except only one.

2. The Bull

A young man once came to Eiríkur and asked for his instruction in magic.

"I don't know any magic, my pet," said Eiríkur. "But you are welcome to stay overnight."

The man accepted.

This was in winter. During the long evening, the cleric approached the would-be student and asked him to go tie his bull, which, he said, had broken loose. The young man assented and went out to the cowshed. A long, narrow corridor, which was only dimly lit, led into it. He heard that the bull was indeed stomping around with angry noises. Nevertheless, the youth entered. But as soon as he was in the corridor, he saw two men who were standing up against the walls, one on either side of the corridor. Both were headless, and they were belaboring each other across the passageway with their bloody lungs. The sight greatly startled the young man, and he stumbled out backward. Running in to Eiríkur, he declared the Devil was loose in the cowshed and he didn't care to get into his clutches.

"Well, my pet," said Eiríkur, "you'll have to move on tomorrow, then."

Another man later sought Eiríkur for the same purpose and was put to the same test. That one was unfazed, saying only when he came upon the ghosts, "You go right on with your work, boys; I just have to squeeze in between you a moment." He then went on in and tied the bull without difficulty.

Going back from the shed, he didn't see the ghosts anywhere. But he did see two big wooden logs where the ghosts had been before.

As he returned to the house, Eiríkur asked him, "Did you tether the bull, my pet?"

"Oh yes, I certainly did," said the other.

"Didn't you see anything on your way?" said Eiríkur.

"Nothing worth mentioning," replied the other.

Eiríkur liked his answer so well that he accepted the man for instruction.

3. The Horse Theft

The Reverend Eiríkur cautioned both shepherds and other boys of Selvogur against taking his horses without permission and warned that they would not fare well if they did. All shepherds therefore refrained from touching his mounts.

Two boys, however, broke the ban. But as soon as they had mounted, the horses set off at a gallop heading directly home to Vogsósar; the boys could not control them. Then, unable to rein in the horses, they tried to throw themselves off, but they couldn't do that either, for their pants were stuck to the horses' backs.

"This is no good," one of them said. "We have to get off the horses, or else we'll get into the Reverend's hands, and that's not an enviable place to be."

Then he took a knife out of his pocket, cut the seat out of his pants, and thereby freed himself. But the other one either couldn't manage to do the same or didn't dare destroy his trousers.

The horses ran home to Vogsósar, one with the screaming boy on its back, the other with the seat of the pants stuck to it. The cleric was outside when the horses arrived. Brushing the piece of cloth from the unmanned horse, he said to the boy riding the other, "It's not much good stealing horses that belong to Eiríkur of Vogsósar, is it? Now get off, and never again take my horses without permission. Your companion was more resourceful; he deserves to be taught a letter or two, for he has the making of a man."

Some time afterward, that boy came to Vogsósar. Eiríkur then showed him the seat from the pants, asking if he recognized it. The lad did not flinch, and he told the parson the truth of what had happened. The cleric smiled. Then he offered the boy a place with him, which he gratefully accepted. He remained with the parson for a long time afterward and was very devoted to him. It is said that Eiríkur taught him a great deal of his ancient lore.

Saints and Sinners

Satan Went to Make a Man

The Devil didn't want to be inferior to God, so he set about creating a man. But the attempt was a disaster, for instead of making a human being, what he turned out was a cat — and a skinless one at that!

Saint Peter took pity on the poor creature, and he made the skin for the cat, as it says in the verse:

> Satan went to make a man,
> but made a skinless cat instead.
> Saint Peter lent a helping hand:
> a hide to dress the quadruped.

In fact, the skin is the only part of the cat that is deemed to be of any use.

The Imp on the Church Beam

Once a minister was holding Sunday services as he did every week. All proceeded correctly and nothing untoward happened until he was in the pulpit and had begun to preach his sermon; then a man in one of the front pews suddenly burst out laughing. The incident was ignored both by the minister and the congregation, and it only happened this once. The minister finished his sermon, left the pulpit for the altar, and performed all the rest of the ritual according to his duty before leaving the church.

When the services were over, the minister began to make inquiries about this man who had scandalized the congregation during the sermon, and he soon found out who he was. So the minister summoned the man and asked him if the words spoken from the pulpit had really been so funny that he had to laugh out loud and shock the congregation. What could be the reason for such behavior, the minister wanted to know.

The man replied that it was far from him to laugh at the minister's teachings; that had never entered his mind. "But I did see something, Reverend," he said, "that you probably didn't, and I doubt if anybody else in the congregation saw it either."

"What was that?" asked the minister.

"Well, Reverend," said the man, "when you had just stepped up into the pulpit, two old crones sitting in the back pew on the women's side fell into an argument and began hurtling abuse and invectives at each other. At that moment I happened to glance up to the church beam, and I saw that an imp had settled himself there. He had a dried-up patch of skin in one hand and a leg-bone of a horse in the other. The imp pricked up his ears at every foul word the crones uttered and listened very attentively, and at the same time he wrote down everything they said on his patch of skin, using the leg-bone as a style. This went on while the scrap of skin lasted, but it finally proved too small. The little devil, however, was resourceful, and he just stretched the patch, holding it with his teeth on the one side and his claws on the other; this way, it lasted him a little while longer, and he went on furiously scribbling away until the skin was all covered. Then he did as before, stretching it and writing some more.

"This repeated itself several times, the imp stretching the patch every which way as he needed more space to write on. The time came, however, when he had used up every last inch of space on the skin and had stretched it to the very limits of its elasticity. But because the old crones were still at it and the imp would by no means miss any of their foul language, he started on the patch once more and stretched it all he could. But as he locked his jaws over the patch on one side, the skin tore, and the imp tumbled over backward off the beam; he probably would have landed square on his behind on the church floor if he hadn't managed to hook his claws into the beam as he was falling. And that, Reverend, was the reason I couldn't contain my laughter, and I should like to ask both you and the congregation most humbly to forgive me if I have caused any scandal."

The minister felt that the man could hardly be blamed for his little breach of decorum and gave him only a mild reprimand — as an example to others. But he wished, he said, those old crones, the next time they came to church, would do something other than entertain the Devil with their abusive language.

72

The Dance at Hruni

Once in olden times there was a priest at Hruni in Árnes County who was very fond of amusements and merrymaking. It was a regular habit of this priest, when people came to church on Christmas Eve, not to hold services during the first part of the night but rather to make his congregation a great ball in the church, with drinking and card-playing and other untoward entertainment until far into the night.

The priest had a mother, advanced in years, by the name of Una. She was much distressed by her son's behavior and often reproved him for it. But he took no heed of it and carried on in his usual way for many years.

Then it happened one Christmas Eve that the priest continued the dance much longer than usual, and his mother, who was both prescient and clairvoyant, went out to the church and asked her son to stop the dancing and begin the mass. The priest, however, thought there was still plenty of time for that. "One more round, mother dear," he said. Thus rebuffed, she returned to the house.

This happened three times: Una went out to her son, pleading with him to remember God and stop before things got out of hand, but he always made the same reply, "One more round, mother dear."

When she had left her son the third time and was heading toward the door of the church, she heard the following verse spoken, and she learned it by heart:

> The music sounds shrill here.
> Sundry people mill here.
> Merrymakers swill here.
> Many coo and bill here.
> Una is still here,
> and Una is still here.

As Una stepped out of the church, she noticed a man outside the door. She did not recognize him but didn't like his looks and felt sure it was he who had spoken the verse. She was much taken aback by the whole affair; it seemed obvious to her that the turn of events had reached a perilous point and that this fellow must indeed be the Devil himself.

So she took her son's mount and rode in great haste to the nearest priest, asking him to come and try to put things right and save

73

her son from impending disaster. The priest returned with her immediately and took many other people with him, for the worshippers at his services had not yet left. By the time they reached Hruni, however, the earth had swallowed the church and the churchyard with all the revelers, whose howling and squealing could be heard from the underground.

There are still visible indications that a building at one time stood up on the Hruni, the hill from which the farm below derives its name. But after this event, the story goes, the church was moved down below the hill to where it now stands. And never again has there been dancing on Christmas Eve in the church at Hruni.

The Parish Pauper

There was once an old woman at a farm. She was a parish pauper, and she was so discontent with her dwelling place that all she could do was harp on it to convince herself how bad it was.

One evening it happened that she was alone in the farmhouse while all the rest of the people were outside tending the livestock. It was winter, and the cold was severe. Then, as the old woman was muttering to herself, a man appeared at her side, and a big, burly fellow he was.

"What a wretched existence you lead here, poor old dear," he said.

"That's no exaggeration," she agreed. "Everybody is mean to me, I get little to eat, and the food is awful. I'm always cold and constantly sick."

"That's an ugly story," said the stranger, "and I'd like to mitigate your distress. I'd like to offer you to come with me because I feel sorry for you, and you won't get a better place than mine if you'd like to try it."

"What an excellent man you are," said the old one. "I should like nothing better than go with you, but I'm so wretched that I can't really walk."

"It doesn't matter," he said. "I can easily take you on my back."

"You are a splendid fellow, indeed," she said, "and you must be enormously strong, too. But," she added, "the thing is I can't go unless I can take my chamberpot with me; I can't be without it."

"It's of no consequence," said the visitor. "I'll take it in my hand."

So it came to pass that the stranger stole out of the farmhouse without anybody knowing it, crone on back and chamberpot in hand. He walked for a good long time. The cold was dreadful, and the old one asked if he wouldn't be home soon.

"Yes, it won't be long now," he said.

Still he continued a long way over hills and hollows, and for the second time the old one wanted to know if he wouldn't soon be home.

"It's a very short way off now," he said.

The old pauper by this time was getting so cold that she could see nothing ahead but freezing to death, and she called out in a loud voice begging God to relieve her of her pains.

No sooner had she uttered the words than she saw the earth open in front of her and the man carrying her sink into it, while she was left sitting at the brink of this enormous chasm looking at the man disappear with her chamberpot in his hand. Then she yelled out, saying, "Damn him, he took my potty."

It is said that the old pauper reached the nearest farm, which wasn't too far off, to tell her tale of woe.

The Ptarmigan

Once upon a time the Virgin Mary summoned all the birds to a meeting. When they arrived, she commanded them to walk through fire. The birds knew that she was the Queen of Heaven and very powerful, so they didn't dare but obey her every wish and command, and all of them darted into the fire at once — all except the ptarmigan. And when they came out of the fire again, all their feet were featherless, singed to the skin, which is how they have remained even to this day. That's what they had for walking through fire for Mary.

But the ptarmigan, the only bird that resisted, fared no better, for Mary became furious and decreed that the ptarmigan be the most defenseless of birds and so victimized that she be forever in fear of her life except on Whitsunday; furthermore, that the falcon, originally meant to have been her brother, should everlastingly pursue and kill her and live off her flesh. But Mary granted the ptarmigan one mercy: that she be able to change colors with the seasons and turn all white in the winter and heather-gray in the summer, so that the falcon should have more difficulty spotting

her in the snow in winter and in the ling meadows in the summertime.

None of this has since failed, nor has the fact that the falcon
pursue, kill, and eat her. Only when he reaches the ptarmigan's
heart does the falcon recognize that she is his sister. At that moment, every time he has killed and eaten one to expose her heart, he
is overcome with such remorse that he howls out his laments for
a long time afterward.

My Jón's Soul

Once upon a time there was an old couple who lived together.
The man was rather a wild sort and had a bad reputation, in addition to which he was lazy and useless to his household. His wife
was very unhappy about this and often scolded him, saying he was
good for nothing but squandering whatever she scraped together, for
she herself was never idle. She turned every trick she knew to earn
their necessities and always managed to come out on top, whomever
she had to deal with. But even though they disagreed on some
things, the woman loved her husband dearly and never let him
want for anything.

This went on for a long time.

One day the old man took to his bed and was very ill. His wife
watched over him. And when he took a turn for the worse, it occurred to her that he was probably not too well prepared for his
death and doubtful if he would be allowed to enter Paradise. So
she thought it might be advisable that she herself try to introduce
her husband's soul. She then took a skin bag and held it over the
old man's face, and when he gave up the ghost, it went straight
into the bag, which the woman immediately tied up with a string.

That done, she set off for Paradise, keeping the bag under her
apron. She soon reached the gates of Heaven and knocked. St.
Peter answered, asking what her business was.

"How do you do," said the old one. "I've come here with my
Jón's soul; you've probably heard of him. I should like you to take
him in."

"Ah, yes, well," said Peter. "Unfortunately, I can't do that. I
certainly *have* heard of that Jón of yours but never anything good."

The old one then replied, "I didn't think, St. Peter, that you of all people would be so heartless. You have obviously forgotten what happened to you in the old days, when you denied your master."

Hearing this, Peter went back in and locked the gates, while the old woman sighed wearily outside.

After a short time, however, she knocked again, and this time St. Paul answered. The woman greeted him and asked his name, which he told her. She then begged him to take care of her Jón's soul, but he said he didn't want to have anything to do with it, remarking that that Jón of hers wasn't worth any grace. This angered the old woman, and she said:

"Look who's talking! I suppose you were more worthy of grace back in antiquity, when you were persecuting God and all good men. I don't think I'll ask you any more."

Paul hastened to lock the gates.

When the old woman knocked for the third time, the Virgin Mary came out.

"How do you do, my dear," said the old one. "I hope that you will let my Jón in, even though Peter and Paul won't allow it."

"I'm very sorry, my good woman," said Mary, "but I just don't dare. He was such a beast, that Jón of yours."

"Oh, I don't blame you," said the old one. "But I thought you of all people would recognize human frailty. Or have you forgotten that you had a child whom you couldn't father?"

Mary didn't care to hear anymore and locked up as quickly as she could.

For the fourth time the old woman knocked at the gates. This time Christ himself came out and asked what she wanted.

She answered meekly, "I wanted to ask you, my beloved Redeemer, to let this wretched soul here inside the door."

Christ answered, "It's Jón, isn't it? No, woman, he didn't believe in me."

As he was speaking, he began to close the gates. But the old woman, acting swiftly, flung the bag with the soul in beside him, and it was swept far into the palace of Heaven before the doors slammed shut. It took a load off the old woman's heart to know that her Jón was, after all, safely inside Paradise, and she joyfully returned to her home.

And that's all we know about the old woman and the soul of her Jón.

Úlfur's Lake

Inland from the valleys of Skagafjördur, in the North, there is a fishing lake called Úlfur's Lake, and here is how it got that name:

There once lived a rich farmer at Maelifellsá. He had a son named Gudmundur, a promising man in every respect, strong and a good wrestler. Gudmundur often went to round up sheep in the mountains and was a leader of the mountain men. At one time, he went on a second search along with some other men and then one day found himself searching with only a boy as a companion. Within sight of Úlfur's Lake, they came across two lambs and began chasing them. The lake was frozen, and they noticed a man lying out on the ice fishing. As the two of them approached, the fisherman got to his feet, took an ax that had been resting beside him, and started gliding over the ice in their direction. Seeing this, the boy took to his heels, but Gudmundur waited for the man. When the stranger got close enough, he struck out at Gudmundur, but he dodged the blow. As he missed his target, the outlaw lost his balance and dropped the ax. Gudmundur managed to reach it and glided out on the ice. The outlaw followed. This went on for a while, until Gudmundur saw an opportunity to turn around and strike his pursuer a fatal blow. As the outlaw was hit, he shouted for Brandur, Thorgils, and Ólafur.

Gudmundur now returned to camp and told his companions what had happened. They went back to the lake in force, but the dead man had disappeared. There were signs that he had been taken away, for they could see a trail of blood leading up from the lake.

After this event, Gudmundur remained at home and did not go rounding up sheep in the mountains, for it was feared that he would be ambushed by the outlaws. But once, late in summer, the shepherd at Maelifellsá was taken ill, and there was no one but Gudmundur to bring home the sheep. He set out to look for them but couldn't find any; going up into the heathlands, he still saw no trace of them. Then he was caught in such a dense fog that he soon didn't know where he was going. He went on nevertheless until he stumbled upon a large knot of sheep and a man standing by. The outlaw immediately flew at Gudmundur, and they wrestled for a long time before Gudmundur managed to fell him. Then the outlaw begged for mercy and promised to do him good in return. Gudmundur asked who he was and where he lived. The outlaw said his name was Ólafur and he was the brother of the man Gudmundur had killed on the lake, whose name had been Úlfur. "There are now six of us brothers left," he said, "and I am the youngest and smallest. My father has a farm not far off, and it was he who charmed you up here in order to pay you back for slaying his son. He has had a grave dug in front of the farmhouse, and he intends for you to rest in it. We have one sister named Sigrídur. My father loves her better than any of us, and she's the one who can be of most help to you — provided she wants to. My brother Brandur is here close by, and if you could wrestle him down, too, so you could claim to have spared both of us, she would give you all the aid she could."

Gudmundur now allowed Ólafur to get up and went on until he found Brandur. They wrestled, and Gudmundur overcame him. Brandur also asked for mercy and promised his help, telling the same story as Ólafur before. So, Gudmundur released him and went on toward the farm. He found Sigrídur outside and gave her regards from her brothers along with their request that she help the one who had spared them. Sigrídur led him up to a loft above the cowshed and gave him wine to drink, which greatly refreshed him. She told him about the pit in front of the house and advised him, when confronted by her father, to retreat from him toward the grave. When he reached it, however, he should jump over it and let her father fall in but spare his life. Now, she said, her father would soon awaken and know that Gudmundur was there. He should walk up to the front of the house and knock on the door.

Gudmundur did as she advised. And when the old man heard the knocking, he got up from his bed remarking that Gudmundur had finally arrived and would soon have his manhood tested. Then he ran outside and, dispensing with greetings, immediately assaulted Gudmundur. A fierce struggle ensued. Gudmundur soon found that he didn't have half the strength of the old man and therefore concentrated on defending himself rather than taking the offensive. The old man wanted to ease him toward the grave, and Gudmundur retreated in that direction. On reaching the edge of the pit, however, Gudmundur jumped over it, while the old man fell headlong in.

At that point, Sigrídur and the two brothers Gudmundur had wrestled before came up and asked him to spare their father. Gudmundur promised to do so, provided that he be left in peace from then on — to which the old man gave his solemn vow; then he was pulled up out of the grave. The old man thanked Gudmundur for sparing his life and asked him inside but said he couldn't guarantee that his elder sons would respect his pledge when they returned home.

Gudmundur was now served with food, and in the evening he was locked inside a hall. The elder brothers returned soon after and asked if Gudmundur was resting in the grave. The old man told them all about what had happened, at which they went mad with rage and wanted to break down the hall door. But the old man planted himself in front of it and told them they would first have to do away with him if they wanted to desecrate his solemn oath. This mollified them, and they went to bed.

In the morning, the old man let them see Gudmundur but forbade them to lunge at him. Gudmundur remained there over the winter, for the way back to Skagafjördur had become impassable. He was attracted to Sigrídur, who was a handsome woman and so strong that she was a match for any of her brothers. And the two of them got along very well together.

In the spring, Gudmundur wanted to return to his home, and Sigrídur wished to go with him, for by that time she was with child. Nor did the old man object. Gudmundur set off with her and didn't rest until he arrived at Maelifellsá. Everyone rejoiced in his return, feeling that he had been reclaimed from the dead.

Gudmundur lived a long time at Maelifellsá, having married Sigrídur, and she was thought to be an outstanding woman. Her brothers gradually moved down to civilization, finding it lonely on their mountain farm after her departure and the death of their father. Some of them became farmers in Skagafjördur, and all were considered men of imposing power.

An Outlaw Killed

It happened in the fall shortly after the Haze Hardships, which began in 1783, that three men of Biskupstungur rode north to the mountains to round up stray sheep. Two of them, named Jón and Nikulás, were farmers; the third one was an adolescent called Bjarni Sveinsson. Jón was getting on in years and a veteran mountain man who had been quite a stalwart and hardy fellow.

The three of them advanced far to the north until they were close to the glaciers. But when they caught sight of four men riding toward them, Jón asked his companions to turn back as fast as they could. Riding through hilly terrain, they had two horses each, all fairly swift, and they made all possible speed.

They had been galloping for some while when they noticed that only one man was still pursuing them. He was riding a roan horse and carrying a cudgel of birch. Jón realized that the stranger was determined to have it out with them, and he dismounted. When the outlaw reached them, he jumped off his horse and struck Nikulás with his cudgel across the hand, rendering it useless. But Jón ran at him, and they hadn't wrestled long before Jón overcame him, for Bjarni had thrown a rope around his feet. Then Jón ordered Bjarni to cut the man's Achilles' tendons. The outlaw let out an enormous scream and threatened to haunt and kill Jón if he slew him. Jón made no answer but drew a knife out of his sleeve and cut the outlaw's throat, working him over in rather a ghastly way, for the fellow struggled fiercely all the while; what surprised Bjarni most was how effectively Jón held him down. In the meantime, Bjarni wanted to take the outlaw's horse, which he had left with the reins up, but Bjarni couldn't catch it, and it ran back with a loud neigh.

Jón placed the outlaw's head by his buttocks, saying he didn't think he would haunt anybody. The man was clad in a cloak of skin, with the fur on the inside, and had a large knife on him. Jón took the knife and told his companions to hurry on as they could. Although the hills had delayed the others in their pursuit, they might still catch up. The three of them took off posthaste and didn't stop until they were back home.

According to Bjarni, he never once saw Jón flinch at his deed, and the rumor was that Jón had previously killed other outlaws during his mountain searches for stray sheep. But he strongly admonished Bjarni not to tell anyone what had happened. And Bjarni told the story quietly to a friend of his only when he was an old man, having married and moved to the North to farm at Fossar in Fossárdalur, which branches out of Svartárdalur in the Húnavatns County.

"Up, My Six, in the Name of Jesus"

Once in the fall six men went up to the mountain pastures on a mop-up search for sheep. Their leader was a big, stalwart man of great courage. When they had reached the farthest parts of the search area, they were caught in a blizzard and lost their way, having no longer any idea where they were.

After a long while they felt they were going downhill and discovered they were in a small valley. Here they came upon a farm and knocked on the door. An old man, very ugly and evil-looking, answered. He told them he was not used to people coming to these parts and snooping around his farm, and he gave his visitors a hostile look. The leader answered on behalf of his men, explaining to the old man how they had come to be there. And without being asked, he made his way inside, along with his companions. The old man neither permitted nor protested their entrance.

When they had been in the house for some while, a young but very sad-looking woman brought them bowls of meat, while the old man watched from the doorway. She whispered to them under her breath, "Eat what's on the farther side of the bowl." They got the impression that there was mutton on that side but human flesh on the other.

Later, the girl cleared the table and, helping them off with their wet clothes, told them, again under her breath, "Be wary. Don't take off your underwear, and don't fall asleep."

It was a moonlit night. The leader of the mountain men lay down in a bed that was all in the shadow, and he told his companions not to stir, no matter what happened, until he called them.

Shortly after they were all in bed, the old man entered the room. He went over to one of the men, felt his chest, and said, "Lean chest, lacking vigor." He felt all the men the same way, mumbling something similar to himself each time.

The last bed he came to was that of the leader, and when he groped about him, the old man said, "Fleshy chest, full valiant."

So saying, he went into a corner of the room, picked up an ax, and returned to the bed. But the leader followed every move he made, and as the old man struck, he rolled out of bed, so the would-be murderer missed him, hitting only the bedclothes. Then he made a grab for the ax and wrested it from the old man.

Deprived of his weapon, the old one yelled out loud, "Up, my twelve, in the name of the Devil!"

Hearing that, the leader brought the ax down on the old man's head, splitting his brain, and said in turn, "Up, my six, in the name of Jesus!"

At that moment a trapdoor opened in the floor and a man's head popped up. The leader chopped it off, and he subsequently slew all twelve of them the same way.

This accomplished, the men looked for the girl who had served them earlier in the evening. She turned out to be a farmer's daughter from Eyjafjördur whom the old man had kidnapped, intending to force her to marry his eldest son. But the girl was revolted by all their ilk, especially because they used to kill and eat all those who lost their way and happened upon the farm.

The men found many valuables in the house, and there was a large number of sheep in the valley. It was decided that their leader and another man should stay behind, both to keep the girl company and to tend the sheep, so they wouldn't perish for lack of care during the winter. The rest of the men returned home.

In the spring, the leader took the girl north to Eyjafjördur and later married her with her father's consent. He brought everything from the remote valley north to her home district, stocked a large farm, and lived a long and prosperous life.

Bjarni Sveinsson and His Sister Salvör

There was a man by the name of Sveinn. He was a farmer in Skagafjördur, in the North. He was married, but the name of his wife is not recorded. Sveinn was a man of some means. He had two children who feature in this story. His son was named Bjarni and his daughter Salvör. They were twins and very fond of each other. At the time of the story, they were about twenty years of age.

One spring around Midsummernight many people of Skagafjördur went to gather Iceland moss in the mountains. Farmer Sveinn thought he would send his son, and when Salvör heard that, she wanted to go as well. Her parents were opposed to it but finally gave in to her pleadings, and it was agreed that both of them go. The night before they were to leave, however, farmer Sveinn had a dream. He dreamed he was the owner of two white birds of which he was very fond. But the female bird was lost, and he missed it very much. Sveinn's interpretation of his dream was that he would soon lose his daughter, and this worried him greatly. He was now totally adverse to her going to the mountains, but she didn't let up until she had her way. So the brother and sister set off together and roamed around the first day picking moss like all the other people. But during the night, Salvör was suddenly taken ill and could no longer go with the others. Bjarni stayed with his sister.

Three days passed, while Salvör got progressively worse and Bjarni never left her side. On the fourth day, he found another man to stay with his sister while he went off by himself. When he had filled his sack with Iceland moss, he sat down under a large boulder and rested his head in his hands. He was thinking about his sister's illness and was very depressed and worried.

Having sat there a short while, Bjarni heard a loud rumbling noise. When he looked around, he saw two men fast approaching on horseback and headed in his direction. One of them was dressed in red and riding a red horse; the other, who was dark-clad, sat a brown horse. They dismounted by the boulder and addressed Bjarni by name. The man in red asked what was wrong, but Bjarni didn't care to tell him. The stranger said there was no harm in talking about it, so Bjarni told him of his sister's illness. He said their co-gatherers were getting ready to return home, "but I have to remain here alone with my sister, and I don't know if she's going to die in my hands."

"You've got trouble, Bjarni," said the man in red, "and you have my sympathy. But how would you like to give me your sister?"

"No," said Bjarni, "I can't do that. I don't know the first thing about you, and I don't know where you come from. Where do you come from?"

"Never mind that," said the red-clad man. He took out a red-gilded silver snuffbox, a stone inlaid in the lid, saying, "Would you sell me your sister for this box?"

"No," said Bjarni. "I'll never give her to you, no matter what you offer."

"Well," said the man, "keep the box anyway as a remembrance of our meeting in the mountains."

Bjarni then took the box and thanked him for it. The visitors said good-bye and rode away, and Bjarni went back to the tent.

In the morning, the other gatherers returned home, and Bjarni remained alone with his sister. He now feared that the strangers might want to kidnap her, and he didn't dare go to sleep. He kept watch over her all day long, but during the following night he grew very drowsy, so he lay down by his sister's side. As a precaution, he locked his arms around her waist, thinking she couldn't be taken without his being awakened. Then he fell fast asleep.

When he woke up again, there was no trace of his sister. Overcome with sadness and remorse, he searched for her all day but didn't find her. So, he folded his tent and rode home during the night to tell his parents what had happened.

"I had that premonition," said his father, Sveinn. "One way or another, fate will have its way."

A party of men was gathered, and an exhaustive search was made, but Salvör was not to be found. Everybody felt it a great bereavement, for the girl had been promising and loved by all.

Time now passed until Bjarni was thirty years of age. By that time, he had married and taken over his father's farm. Then it happened one fall that his shepherd lost his entire flock of sheep and couldn't find it even though he searched for three days. Bjarni then asked his wife to prepare a week's supply of food for him, along with a good pair of shoes, for he said he would go looking for his sheep. Bjarni's parents were still alive, and they pleaded with him not to go. But he told them not to fear and not to expect him back in less than a week's time. After that he left, walking without rest for a day and a half. Then he came upon a cave and lay down to sleep.

When he woke up again, a pitch-dark fog had descended, and he had no sooner set off than he lost his directions. Nevertheless, he kept on walking until he found himself in a fairly large valley. It was then late in the day. There was no fog in the valley, and once down there, Bjarni saw a large and stately farmhouse. He headed for it. Seeing men and women making hay outside the homefield, he walked over to the women; there were three of them, one of whom was by far the noblest-looking. Greeting them, Bjarni asked if he might be allowed to stay overnight. They all said yes to his question, and one of them, a young girl, very pretty, took him home to the farmhouse. It occurred to Bjarni that she resembled his sister, whom he had lost gathering Iceland moss in the mountains years before. The whole event came back to him, and he became very sad, although he kept it to himself.

Home at the farmhouse, the girl led Bjarni inside. The interior was large and attractive. The girl took him into a sizable, well-furnished room, offered him a chair, and asked him to wait. Then she ran out but returned instantly, bringing food and wine which she placed before Bjarni. When he had eaten, the girl told him he could go to bed if he liked. She led him to a small room where there was a bed already made. Bjarni undressed, and the girl helped him take off his wet clothes, then bid him good-night, and left.

Bjarni wondered where he might be and how the girl could have so made him recall his great sorrow; but he couldn't understand it. From such thoughts, he fell asleep but was awakened again by singing from above. He heard that on the loft above his bed, someone was reading a sermon as was common in the countryside. The singers were many, both men and women, yet one voice surpassed all the others. This voice stirred up the depth of Bjarni's sorrow, for he felt he recognized in it the tone of his sister Salvör. He pondered this for a while, but then he fell asleep again, and the next thing he knew the little girl who had shown him to bed the evening before was there awakening him. She brought him good clothes and asked him to put them on, saying he would stay the day because it was Sunday. With that, she left.

While Bjarni was dressing, a small lad came into his room. He was wearing a green woolen tunic and well dressed in every respect. The boy greeted Bjarni and was very talkative.

"Where are you going?" he asked.

"I am looking for my sheep," said Bjarni.

"I haven't seen any of them here in the valley," said the lad. "You will stay with us today," he added, "for my father is going to hold services."

Just then, the girl entered, saying, "Sveinn, stop pestering the man with your nonsense." She brought Bjarni breakfast.

When he had eaten, Bjarni went outside. He saw that a great many people were arriving. The lad took him by the hand, led him over to the church, and ushered him to a seat. Looking around him, Bjarni recognized the man in red who had come to him in the mountains sitting at his side. And the minister, he noticed, was the man who at that time had worn dark clothes. Many people were in church, and most of the men were large and evil-looking. Some of them were in clothes knitted from naturally black wool.

Bjarni pulled out his silver box and offered his neighbor some snuff, which was accepted. In the nave of the church he saw a woman, elegantly dressed, and thought he recognized his sister. They looked at each other, and it appeared as though she alternately smiled and wept at seeing him. Then he felt he understood how it all fitted together and that he had found his sister again.

The service now began and was very well conducted. After the final blessing, the lad took Bjarni by the hand and led him out. An old, evil-looking man was sitting outside the door. He stuck out his foot, tripping Bjarni so he fell. The lad immediately ran back into the church and brought out the red-clad man. He seized the old one by the chest and shook him, while the boy took Bjarni into the farmhouse.

Before long, they were joined there by the man in red and the one in blue, both of whom greeted Bjarni in a friendly manner, asking if he recognized them. He said he did but remained rather cool toward them, for many things had come back to him. But just at that moment, the woman he had seen in church and taken for his sister entered. She ran to embrace Bjarni and said, "I was in your arms in the womb, and crying was I severed from you, but now I come laughing into your arms again, my brother."

They now greeted each other dearly, rejoicing in their reunion, and he told her everything that had happened in Skagafjördur since her disappearance. Then the man in red added, "I took your sister from your arms that time, Bjarni, and married her to this blue-clad man. He is my son and our minister here in the valley, while I am the magistrate. This time, I took your sheep and made you stray here so the two of you could see each other and catch up on what has happened to you since you were parted. Tomorrow, I'll take you back and give you your sheep, but stay here overnight and talk to your sister."

Bjarni did as he suggested.

Leaving the morning after, he said a tearful good-bye to his sister. The man in red escorted him and helped drive the sheep. The one in blue went along, too, and both of them accompanied Bjarni most of the way home. They parted with words of mutual friendship. The dark-clad man said he would send for Bjarni in the spring and asked him to be ready when Moving Days arrived. "You will live with us in the valley," he said. Upon his return home, Bjarni told his wife and his parents all about his journey and about his intentions but asked them to keep it to themselves. Time then passed until Moving Days. At that juncture, three men came to Bjarni's farm with packhorses. He left during the night with all his livestock, his old parents, wife, and children. They arrived in the valley to the joy of the whole family. Bjarni lived there a long time. When he was getting on in years, however, he returned to Skagafjördur. He told this story before dying at a ripe old age.

Visitation by the Bishop of Skálholt

A bishop of Skálholt once made a tour of visitations north to the Múla County. In the mountains, he was caught in fog and lost his way. For a long while, he rode on with his party, and finally they reached a small valley where they came upon a neatly built farmhouse. They knocked at the door, and an old man answered. The bishop assumed that he was the master of the house and asked shelter for the night for himself and his men. The farmer replied rather dryly that they could unsaddle their horses and were free to enter the *badstofa*.

They did so.

Inside, they met an old woman and a young girl. Twelve clods of sod, covered with sheepskins, were in the *badstofa*, on which the bishop and his men were offered places; as it happened, there was just the right number. The old couple and the young girl were seated on a low dais across the end of the room. Everyone was silent, for the bishop had ordered his men to keep their peace.

In a little while the women stepped down. They served the bishop and his entourage fresh meat in wooden bowls and then hot sheep's milk in other bowls, together with wooden spoons. This was in the middle of summer, and yet the milk was as thick as it is generally only in the fall. Everything inside was skillfully crafted, clean, and attractive. As the girl cleared the table afterward, she whispered to the bishop that everything would be well if no one showed any suspicion and everyone kept calm, whatever happened.

In the evening, the bishop and his men were led to sleeping quarters in an outer hall. It had twelve beds made with sheepskin spreads, pillows, and coverings under and over; they were soft and warm as well as roomy. The bishop lay down in the innermost place and his men toward the front, each in his individual bed. The bishop reminded them quietly that they should keep their composure and not get excited, no matter what happened.

Shortly afterward, they heard footsteps and voices, and in a little while the old man entered, holding a light in one hand and a knife in the other. He shone the light in the face of each of the men, including the bishop, pointing his knife at them. Then he left, and they heard him say, "They may be trusted; otherwise, they would have attacked me when I was alone."

In the morning, they saw twelve other men with the old one. They appeared to be middle-aged and younger, all of them vigorous-looking and resembling each other. The old man was much more cheerful than he had been the day before. The weather was overcast, with sleet and rain, so the old man invited the bishop to stay another night, which he accepted.

During the day, the old man asked the bishop a good many things, among them which had been the most populous Althing that he had attended.

"That was more than forty years ago, now," said the bishop, "when I was a mere boy of eighteen. It happened that a brother and a sister from Midfjördur were scheduled to be executed for having had a child together. But as they were convicted and the sentence was being read, many people rushed up to hear it, and in the confusion the man saw an opportunity to bridle a brown horse he owned, jump upon it, and gallop off with his sister behind him. Guards and many others also took their horses and rode after him. They pursued him for three days through the hills, over lava beds, rocks, and ravines. The last they saw of him was that he rode into a large lake with what looked like sheer cliffs on the other side. He disappeared near the cliffs, but they couldn't see the end of the lake, and no one dared follow."

The day after, the bishop resumed his journey, and the old man saw him off. He told the bishop his name was Magnús and that he was the very man the bishop had seen at the Althing, who had fled with his sister. He said they had ceased their flight in this little valley, found sheep grazing, and kept them as their livestock. The old woman, he said, was his sister, and the young girl and the twelve men their children. He also said that he had arranged for the bishop to find him, for in the following winter he and his sister would die, and he wanted to ask the bishop to find places for their offspring; otherwise, they would turn into mad heathens up there in the mountains.

The bishop promised to do this, and the following spring he had the family moved. He settled the brothers in various places and married off their sister. The bodies of the old sibling couple were removed to Skálholt and interred there.

90

Miscellaneous Tales

The Grímsey Man and the Polar Bear

Once during the winter it happened on the island of Grímsey
that all the fires died out and couldn't be rekindled at any of the
farms. The weather was calm at the time and the cold so severe
that the Grímsey Sound had frozen over and was thought to be
passable on foot. The people then decided to send some men to the
mainland to get fire, and they chose three of the doughtiest men
on the island for the journey. The three set out early in the morning
in clear weather, and a great many of the islanders followed them
out on the ice to see them off, wishing them a good journey and a
speedy return.

The emissaries' journey was uneventful until, about midway
across the Sound, they came upon a crack in the ice that stretched
out in both directions as far as the eye could see, and it was so
wide that two of them could barely jump across it; the third one
felt unable to. The first two then advised the third to return to the
island and they continued on their way, while he was left on the
other side gazing after them into the distance. Loath to turn back
without trying further, however, he decided to walk along the crack
in case it might be narrower some other place.

As the day wore on, the sky grew overcast, and the wind turned
southerly with a rainstorm. The ice began to break up, and finally
the man was left on a floe drifting out to sea. In the evening, the
floe ran into a large ridge of ice, and the man scrambled onto it.
There he saw a female polar bear lying with her cubs a short distance off. Already cold and hungry, he now feared for his life.

When the bear caught sight of the man, she looked at him for
a while. Then she got up, sauntered over to him and around him,
and indicated he should lie down in the lair with her cubs. He did
with great trepidation. Then the animal lay down with him, spread
herself around him, got him onto her teats, and had him suckle
her along with her cubs.

So the night passed.

The day after, the she-bear got up and walked a stone's throw
from the lair, beckoning the man to follow. Out on the ice, she lay

down at his feet indicating that he climb up on her back. When he had done so, the creature got up again and shook herself wildly until the man fell off. She made no further attempt for the time being, and the man was greatly surprised at this game.

Three days passed. The man huddled in the lair each night with the she-bear, suckling her, and every morning she had him climb on her back and then shook herself until he could hold on no longer. On the morning of the fourth day, the islander managed to stay on the animal's back no matter how she tried to shake him off. Then, in the afternoon, she lowered herself into the sea, the man on her back, and swam with him over to Grímsey.

Once ashore, the man walked up on the island beckoning the bear to follow. He went straight to his home, immediately had his best cow milked, and gave the bear as much as she wanted to drink. Then, with the bear following him, he strode off to his sheep cot, had two of his biggest and best wethers killed, bound them together by their horns, and slung them across the animal's back. That done, the she-bear returned to the sea and swam out to her cubs.

This was a moment of great joy in Grímsey, for while the astonished islanders watched the bear recede into the distance, they also saw a boat under full sails swiftly approaching the island, and they were certain that it was bringing back the other two emissaries with the fire.

Tale of a Raven

Story has it that several farms of Vatnsdalur, in the North, were ruined by landslides from the so-called Vatnsdalur Mountain. Among them was one named Gullberastadir. The farmer living there at the time had a daughter who was in the habit of giving a little something to the farm raven whenever she had a meal.

One day, as usual, she handed her bit of food out through the window, but the raven would not accept it. The girl wondered what was wrong, and she took the food outside. The raven came up very close to her but then hopped off again without eating, although it still acted as if it wanted to. In this manner, the girl gradually followed the raven down over the homefield some distance from the farmhouse.

When they had reached a certain spot, she heard a great big

rumble up in the mountain, and before she could turn around, the landslide came down on both sides of them, while the spot they were standing on was spared. The farmhouse was completely buried.

This was how the raven repaid the farmer's daughter for the food. But the reason why the landslide didn't fall over the spot where they stood is said to be that once, when Bishop Gudmundur was traveling, he had pitched his tent on the site, and before he left, he had consecrated the campsite as he used to do in many other places.

It is further told that about three years later, as a certain shepherd was traveling that way, he rode over the scree where the farmhouse had stood. Then his horse stepped into a hole, and the shepherd, reflecting, imagined he must have ridden over the farmhouse which had caved in. He therefore took a closer look at the hole and smelled a dreadful stench coming out of it. Suspecting the reason, he then piled up a small cairn to mark the spot.

When he arrived at his home, he told what had happened, and people went and widened the hole so it could be entered. It proved to be the farmhouse larder, and there was a woman still in it barely alive. She had supposedly been there when the landslide fell, but the larder wasn't completely leveled because it had been newly rebuilt. And she was able to survive in it because the slide had occurred in the fall when all the provisions for the winter had been stored.

The Sealskin

There once was a man in Mýrdalur who happened to be walking by the sea cliffs one morning early, while most other people were still in bed. Then he came upon the mouth of a cave. Sounds of gaiety and dancing were heard from inside the cave, while outside it a great many sealskins were lying about. The man took one of the skins, carried it home with him, and locked it away in a trunk.

Later in the day he went by the cave again. This time a young, beautiful woman was sitting there, stark naked and crying bitterly: She was the seal whose skin the man had taken. After he had brought her some clothes, the man comforted her and took her home with him. She became quite attached to him but didn't get on too well with others. Many times, she would sit and gaze out over the sea.

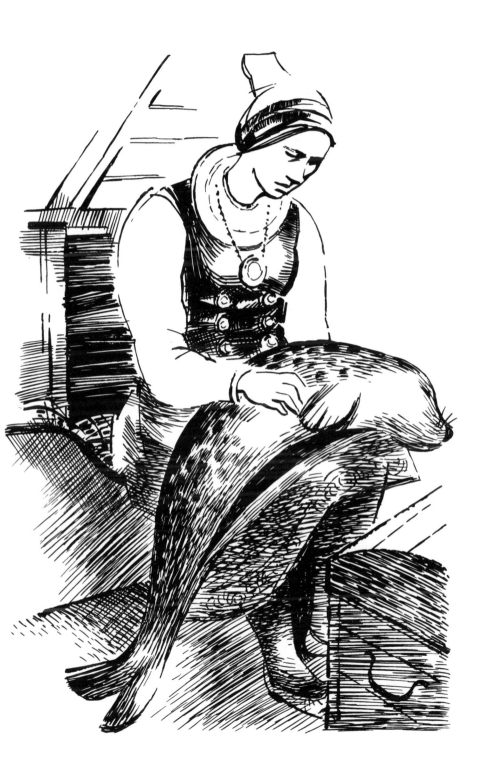

After some time had passed, the man married her. They proved to be quite compatible and had several children. The husband always kept the skin locked away in his trunk and carried the key with him wherever he went.

One day, many years later, he went out to fish and forgot the key under his pillow. Others say that he went to Christmas services, along with his household, while his wife, who was not feeling well, remained at home, and that he forgot to take the key from the pocket of his work clothes when he changed. Whichever way it was, when he returned home, the trunk was open and his wife, along with the sealskin, gone. She had taken the key, looked into the trunk out of curiosity, and found the skin. Unable to resist the temptation, she then had said good-bye to her children, put on the skin, and plunged into the sea. But before she did, the story goes, she recited these words, as if to herself:

"Of two minds must I be:
I've seven children in the sea
and seven more on land."

The husband is said to have grieved for her deeply.

Later, when he went out fishing, a seal would often circle around his skiff, and sometimes it looked as if tears were running from its eyes. The man had the best of luck in his fisheries ever after, and the sea washed many things up on his shore. People often noticed that when his children happened to be walking on the beach, a seal would swim offshore along with them and throw them multicolored fish and pretty seashells.

But never again did their mother return to land.

The Serpent of Lagarfljót

At one time, long, long ago, there was a woman living on a farm in the Lagarfljót district, close by the stream where it broadens into a lake. She had a grown daughter. Once, she gave her daughter a gold ring.

The girl said to her, "Mother, how can I make the most out of this gold?"

"Put it under a ling snake," said the woman.

So, the girl secured a ling snake and put it in her linen chest, the gold underneath it. There it lay for a few days. But when the girl went to look at her ring again, the snake had grown so large that the chest was beginning to come apart. Then the girl was frightened, and she picked up the chest with everything in it and threw it into the lake. A long time passed.

Gradually, people became aware that there was a serpent in the lake, for it was beginning to kill both people and animals crossing the waters. Sometimes it would even reach up on the banks, spewing its venom around most fearfully. It was soon obvious that this was a potentially big problem, but no one knew how to solve it.

Finally, two Finns were summoned to kill the serpent and recover the gold. They dived into the lake but soon came back up again. The task, they declared, was totally beyond them. Neither could this serpent be killed, said the Finns, nor the gold retrieved, for there was another snake beneath the gold, half again as fierce as the first one. So they did the next best thing: chained the serpent down with two fetters, one behind the flippers and another around the tail. The serpent, therefore, can no longer kill man or beast, but sometimes it will arch its back, and when this is seen, it is always taken to augur disaster.

Those who do not believe in the serpent, however, say it is a mere figment of the imagination, and they quote a story about a certain minister who not very long ago rowed straight across the spot where the serpent seemed to be in order to prove his contention that it doesn't exist.

The Convent at Kirkjubaer

This cloister is located in the South, in the Sída district of the Skaftafell County. The *Book of Settlements* states that the site was inhabited by the *papar*, that is, Christians, before Iceland was settled by the Norsemen. So sacrosanct was the place, already in the Age of Settlement, that it was commonly believed that no heathen might live there. And as fortune would have it, Ketill the Foolish, who settled there and raised his farm at Kirkjubaer, was indeed a Christian. But after Ketill died, a heathen by the name of Hildir, discounting the common belief, decided to move his household to the site. When he arrived at the edge of the homefield, he fell down dead and was buried in Hildir's Mound, which lies east of Kirkjubaer. A convent was established at Kirkjubaer in 1186. The following tales have been told about it:

Above Kirkjubaer lies a beautiful mountainside covered with grass up to the crowning cliffs, which may be climbed in many places, steep though they are. Up on the mountain, there are large stretches of lovely grassland around a lake called Systravatn — Sisters' Lake — because two nuns from the convent are supposed to have gone there, either both together or singly. The story goes that an extraordinarily beautiful comb of gold had been mysteriously held up from the waters of the lake and one of the nuns tried to wade out for it. But the lake was too deep, and she perished. The other one is said to have coveted the comb as well but couldn't see any way of getting it. Finally, she caught sight of a stone-gray horse by the lake and decided to ride it. But the horse was so large that she couldn't mount it until it lowered its front part or got down on its knees. Then she rode it out into the lake, and none of them has since been seen, the nun, the horse, or the comb. For this reason, the lake is called Systravatn.

While Agatha Helgadóttir was mother superior of the Kirkjubaer convent, some strange happenings occurred there. For a long time during the summer of 1336, loud moans were heard from under the bed- and dining-room floors at Kirkjubaer, but nothing was ever found, even though a search was made. The same year as Mother Agatha died, in 1343, the newly ordained Bishop Jón Sigurdsson came from abroad, landing at Reydarfjördur in the East. From there, he immediately began his visitations, going through the South toward the West, and on the way he stopped at Kirkjubaer. At that time, a sister named Katrín was burnt at the stake for godlessness and other serious charges of which she was proven guilty. First, that she had pledged herself to the Devil in writing; second, that she had mishandled the body of Christ (consecrated bread) by throwing it behind a toilet door; third, that she had lain with numerous laymen. And so it was adjudged that she be burnt at the stake.

Some say that two sisters were burnt at this time, the second one for maligning the Pope or not speaking of him with sufficient reverence, and so she had been burnt along with Katrín.

The river Skaftá flows hard by Kirkjubaer, and west of it a single, sheer cliff rises out of the ground, the only ascent being on one side of it. On the top, there is a small, flat lawn with two

98

hummocks, which people say are the graves of the sisters. They had been burnt there, the story goes, and one hummock always remains green while the other one never is and is covered only with thistles. For this reason, the cliff is called Systrastapi — Sisters' Bluff.

Contemporaneous with the nuns' convent at Kirkjubaer, there was a monastery at Thykkvibaer in Álftaver, no more than a mile and a quarter away, as the crow flies. But as well known, the Skaftá flows between the Sída and the Álftaver. In former ages, there was a bridge over the river, and it was the obligation of the convent at Kirkjubaer to maintain it, wherefore all the driftwood washed up on the stretch of shore still called Brúarfjara — Bridge Shore — was assigned to the convent. In later times, the bridge collapsed, but the site is still called Brúarhlad — Bridge Ramp; it is now a regular fording place on the Skaftá.

It is said that the abbot and the monks of Thykkvibaer often went up to Kirkjubaer to see the mother superior and the sisters, and this was not difficult when the bridge was still intact. On the way, south or west of the river, there is a place named Sönghóll — Song Hill — which affords the first view of Kirkjubaer if this route is taken. When the monks reached this hill, they customarily began singing so forcefully that it could be heard at the convent, and it is from this that the hill still derives its name. When the song was heard at Kirkjubaer, the mother superior had the bells rung, while she and all the sisters went down to Skaftá to greet the abbot and the monks. In this place, there are now only sandy craters to be seen, and the tract is called Glennarar — Striders.

It was always a glorious time at Kirkjubaer when the men from Thykkvibaer visited, and the sisters never felt as happy in their life as on those occasions. But the rumor soon began to spread that the monks were going there more often than was proper and were seducing the sisters. This conduct went so far that the mother superior and the sisters all knew about one another, and thereof a few tales are still told. Once, it is said, the abbot of Thykkvibaer had stayed overnight at Kirkjubaer, as often before. In the morning, some sisters came into the mother superior's cell and prepared to dress her. Then, looking for her underwear at the head of the bed, they came across the abbot's underpants, but nowhere could they find the mother superior's shift. Recognizing the abbot's garment, they asked how it had gotten there — to which the mother superior is supposed to have answered, "We all have our failings."

Another time, both the abbot and one or more of the monks spent the night at Kirkjubaer. To begin with, no one knew where the abbot had made his bed, but the story goes that in the middle of the night the mother superior went with a light to check on the propriety of the sisters' conduct. Then, in one cell, she came upon a monk and a nun sleeping together. The mother superior was about to reprimand the nun when the latter noticed her superior's headgear and said, "What is that you have on your head, dear mother?" Then the mother superior realized that she had taken the abbot's underpants by mistake and put them on her head instead of her bonnet. As a result, she softened her voice, saying as she retreated, "We're all sinners, sister."

The River Öxará

It used to be a popular belief that the river Öxará turned into wine for an hour each year. Once it happened that two priests at Thingvellir were up late on New Year's Eve. One of them was a young man, and he was writing a sermon for New Year's Day. The other, an elderly fellow, was sitting with his colleague to keep him company.

About midnight, the younger priest became very thirsty, so he ran out to Öxará with a bottle and filled it with water from the river. But when he returned home with it and looked at the water, he saw it was the color of wine. So he took a sip, and sure enough, the bottle was filled with the finest wine.

The two priests now had a drink or two from the bottle and then put it aside on the window sill. A while later, intending to enjoy the rest of the wine in it, they again reached for the bottle, but then it contained only water pure and clear. This, they thought, was a great wonder, and they discussed it back and forth between them. The younger priest vowed to test the wine in the river at the same time the following year.

Time now passed until the next New Year's Eve. Both the priests stayed up, and at midnight the younger one went out with his bottle and filled it in the river. When he returned home, he thought its contents were blood-colored. He took a sip to taste it and convinced himself there was only blood in the bottle. Having established that, the priest put down the bottle but picked it up again a little later, at which time the bottle held mere water and no blood. The two clerics discussed this for a long time but came no closer to understanding the transformations of the river. It was a common belief that the Öxará turned to blood if many people were destined to be slain at the Althing. And it is said that the following spring, while the Althing was in session, there was indeed a great battle in which a vast number of men were killed.

The Story of Prince Hlini

Once upon a time there was a king and a queen in their kingdom. His name was Hringur, but the queen's name is not known. They had one son called Hlini. He showed great promise at an early age and grew up to be quite a champion. The story has it that there was a cotter and his wife living near the palace grounds. They had a daughter named Signý.

One day it happened that the prince went out hunting with some of his father's retainers. When they had felled a few animals and several birds and were preparing to return home, a fog descended upon them so dense that the men lost sight of the prince. After searching in vain a very long time, they went back to the palace and told the king they had lost Hlini and couldn't find him anywhere. The news greatly saddened the king, and the day after he sent out a large party of men to look for his son. They searched until evening without finding him, and this went on for three days; Hlini was nowhere to be found. The king became sick with grief and took to his bed. He let it be known throughout his realm that whoever could find his son would be rewarded with half his kingdom.

When Signý heard of this, she told her parents, asked them for food and new footwear — which they gave her — and immediately set off. She walked for the better part of a day, and toward evening she came upon a cave. Entering it, she saw two beds, one embroidered with silver and the other with gold. When she looked closer, she saw the prince lying in the gold-embroidered one. She tried to wake him but couldn't. Then she took a better look around her and saw there were runes scored on the beds, spelling out words she didn't understand. Then she went and hid in the nook behind the cave door.

No sooner was she there than she heard a great rumble and saw two very large-featured giantesses coming. As they stepped into their cave, one of them said, "Fy, fo, there's a smell of humans in our cave."

"It is of Prince Hlini," said the other.

They went up to the bed where the prince was resting and said:

"Sing, sing, my swans,
sing Prince Hlini awake."

The swans sang, and Hlini woke up. The younger giantess asked him if he wanted something to eat. He said no. Then she asked if he wanted to marry her. He said no. Hearing that, she shouted out:

"Sing, sing, my swans,
sing Prince Hlini to sleep."

They sang, and he fell asleep. The giantesses then undressed and went to sleep in the silver-embroidered bed.

When they got up the following morning, they roused Hlini and offered him food, which he rejected. Then the younger one asked if he would marry her. He said no, and with that they put him to sleep the same way as before and left.

Shortly after they were gone, Signý crawled out of her nook and woke the prince the way the giantesses had. He greeted her warmly and asked the news. She told him whatever she knew and then asked him to tell her what had happened. He said that when he had been parted from his men, he had met the two giantesses, and they had taken him to this place, where, as Signý must have heard, one of them wanted to force him to wed her. To this, Signý said, "You should promise to marry her on the condition that she tell you what the carvings on the beds mean and what the two of them do all day."

The prince said he would.

Thereupon, he took a chessboard that was there and asked Signý to play with him. They played until evening, but when dusk began to fall, she put him to sleep and returned to her nook. Shortly after, she heard the giantesses coming, and they soon slouched into the cave, monstrous-looking as they were, and the older one cooked a meal. The younger one went over to the bed, woke Hlini, and asked if he would eat. This time, he accepted. When he had finished his food, the giantess asked him if he would marry her. He replied that he would, provided that she tell him the meaning of the runes on the two beds. The giantess told him they meant:

Glide, glide, my good bed
wherever I want to go.

That was all very good, he said, but she would have to tell him more — namely, what the two of them were doing in the woods all day long. She said they were hunting for birds and animals, but in between they would sit beneath an oak tree and toss their life egg back and forth between them. He asked what happened if it broke. Then, the giantess said, they would both die. Hlini told her she had done well confiding in him, but now, he said, he would like to rest until morning.

"As you wish," answered the giantess.

In the morning, she woke the prince for breakfast, which he accepted. Then she offered him to come out to the woods with them, but he told her he preferred to stay home. So the giantess said good-bye and put him to sleep. After that, she left with her companion.

A good while after they had gone, Signý went to awaken the prince. "Now, let's go out to the woods where the giantesses are," she said. "You take your spear with you, and when they start tossing their egg, throw the spear at it, and be sure not to miss. Your life depends on it."

The prince agreed to her plan, and they both stood up on the bed, saying:

"Glide, glide, my good bed
out to the woods."

The bed took off at once and didn't stop until they reached a large oak tree in the woods. There, Signý and Hlini heard a roaring laughter. Signý told the prince to climb up in the tree. He did and saw the two giantesses below, one of them holding a golden egg. She tossed it to the other. At the same time, the prince threw his javelin, and it struck the egg, breaking it. The giantesses gave a start and fell sideways, foaming at the mouth.

Then the prince descended from the oak, and he and Signý went back to the cave. They took everything that was of value, loaded it onto the beds, and returned to Signý's cottage with all the wealth. The cotter and his wife greeted them warmly and bid them welcome. Prince Hlini stayed at the cottage overnight.

Early the next morning, Signý went to the palace, stood before the king, and hailed him. The king asked who she was. She said she was the cotter's daughter from just outside the palace grounds and then went on to ask what he would say if she brought him back his son. The king replied that the question didn't even merit an answer, for she would hardly be able to find him "since none of the men in my realm have been able to." Signý asked again whether he would reward her the same way as he had promised the others if she brought home the prince. The king said he would.

With that, Signý went back to the cottage and bid the prince accompany her to the king's palace, where she led him before his father. The king greeted his son with great affection and asked him to tell what had happened to him since the time he was parted from his men. Hlini sat down on a throne, inviting Signý to sit beside him, and began his story. He told it exactly as it has been told here, adding that he owed his life to Signý. So saying, the prince asked his father's permission to marry her. The king gave his consent and had a banquet prepared, to which he invited all the noblest people of the kingdom. It was a beautiful feast that lasted for a week, and at the end of it all the guests returned to their homes praising the king's generosity.

The prince and Signý loved each other long and well. And so ends this story.

Búkolla and the Boy

Once there was a man who lived with his wife in a cottage. They had one son, but they weren't very fond of him. There were only the three of them in the cottage. The couple also had a cow, which was all their livestock. The cow was called Búkolla.

One day the cow had a calf, and the woman herself sat with her while she was delivering. When the cow had calved and had recovered, the woman dashed into the house. A little later she returned to the barn to see how the cow was doing, but by then, Búkolla had disappeared. The man and his wife went out at once to look for the cow, and they searched for it both far and wide but to no avail. On their return, they were in a foul mood and told the boy to get out and not come within their sight again until he brought

104

back the cow. They packed him some food for the road and gave him new shoes, and with that he set off.

He walked for a long time until he became hungry and sat down to eat. In his desperation, he said out loud, "Moo now, my dearest Búkolla, if you're alive anywhere!"

From far, far away, he heard the cow's response.

Again, the boy walked for a long time before he sat down to have another bite. Then he repeated, "Moo now, my dearest Búkolla, if you're alive anywhere."

This time he heard the cow respond somewhat closer than before.

Once more the boy walked for a long time until he reached the brink of an enormously high precipice. Having walked up an appetite, he sat down to eat, again saying as before, "Moo now, my dearest Búkolla, if you're still alive somewhere."

The cow's response now came from right under his feet.

Somehow, the boy clambered down the precipice, and reaching the bottom, he saw a large cave carved out of it. He went in, and there, bound to a low partition, he found Búkolla. He untied the cow immediately, led her out, and set off back home.

The boy had gone only a small part of the way when he saw that a huge ogress was coming after him, accompanied by another smaller one. He realized at once that the big ogress, with her long strides, would catch up with him in no time, and he said, "What are we to do now, my dearest Búkolla?"

"Pick a hair from my tail, and put it on the ground," said the cow.

He did.

Then the cow said to the hair, "By these words I lay the spell that you become a stream so large that no one can cross it but the bird on its wing."

At the very instant, the hair turned into a tremendous stream.

When the ogress reached the bank of the stream, she said, "You won't get away with that, my boy." And she told the little ogress, "Run home, girl, and get your father's big bull."

The young one ran off and soon returned with an enormous bull, which instantly drank up the whole stream.

Again, the boy feared that the ogress would overtake him very quickly because of her long strides, and he said, "What are we to do now, my dearest Búkolla?"

"Pick a hair from my tail, and put it on the ground."

He did just that.

Then Búkolla said to the hair, "By these words I lay the spell that you become a blaze so hot that no one can cross it but the bird on its wing."

As soon as she had spoken, the hair turned into a big fire.

When the ogress reached the blazing wall, she shouted, "You won't get away with that, my boy." And to the smaller ogress she said, "Go get your father's big bull, girl."

The girl did and returned with the bull, which then urinated all the water it had drunk from the stream and thus put out the fire.

Once more, the boy saw that the ogress would catch up with him very soon because of the length of her strides, and he said, "What are we to do now, my dearest Búkolla?"

"Pick a hair from my tail, and put it on the ground," she said. Then, to the hair, "By these words I lay the spell that you become a mountain so big that no one can surmount it but the bird on its wing."

The hair immediately turned into such a huge mountain that the boy could see only straight up into the sky.

When the ogress came to the mountain, she roared, "You won't get away with that, my boy." To the smaller ogress she said, "Go get me your father's big drill, my girl."

Off went the young one, returning with the drill. The ogress then bored a hole straight through the mountain. But when she could see through it, she became a bit too rash. She squeezed herself into the hole, which was too narrow for her, and got stuck. Finally, she turned into stone right there in the hole. And that's where she remains to this day.

As for the boy, he reached the cottage safe and sound with his Búkolla, and the old couple was quite relieved to have them both back.

"My Old Lady Wants Something for Her Whorl"

Once upon a time there was an old man who lived with his wife in a cottage. They were very poor. The only thing they had of value was a whorl of gold on the old woman's spindle. To get them something to eat, the old man used to go out every day hunting or fishing.

Not far from the cottage, there was a single large mound. It was popular belief that it was inhabited by an elf called Kidhouse, who was considered a crafty fellow and someone to be wary of.

106

One day, as innumerable times before, it happened that the old man went out hunting, while the old lady stayed home as usual. It was a fine day, and she sat down outside the hut with her spindle to spin for a while. Then, by accident, the gold whorl fell from the spindle and rolled off somewhere so the old woman lost sight of it. This annoyed her more than a little, and she looked for it all over but to no avail; she couldn't find the whorl anywhere.

Shortly afterward, the old man returned home, and she told him her misfortune. The man said Kidhouse probably took it; that would be just like him. And with that, he made ready to leave again, telling his wife that he was going to claim the whorl from Kidhouse, or at least get something for it. This cheered the old lady a little bit.

Without further ado, then, the old man went straight to Kidhouse's mound and beat on it long and unsparingly with a cudgel. At long length, Kidhouse answered.

"Who's that banging on my house?" he asked.

The old man replied, "It's your neighbor next door. My old lady wants something for her whorl."

Kidhouse asked what he wanted for it, and the old man requested a cow that would yield ten quarts per milking, which Kidhouse granted him. The old man returned home, bringing his wife the cow.

The day after, having milked the cow in the evening and in the morning and filled all her pots and tubs with milk, the old woman thought she would make some porridge. But then she remembered that she had no grain for it. So she went to her husband and asked him to go see Kidhouse and request some grain for her porridge.

The old man went to Kidhouse and beat the mound as he had done before.

Kidhouse answered, "Who's that banging on my house?"

The man said, "It's your neighbor next door. My old lady wants something for her whorl."

Kidhouse asked him what he wanted, and the old man begged some grain for the pot, for the old lady wanted to make porridge. Kidhouse gave him a barrel of grains, the old man took it home, and his wife made the porridge.

When it was ready, the couple sat down to eat and consumed as much as they could. But having eaten all they could manage, they still had a great deal left in the pot. Then they began to ponder what they should do with the leftovers, and they thought it would be nice to bring them to their beloved Saint Mary. They soon realized, however, that it wouldn't be easy to get up to her on high, so they agreed to ask Kidhouse for a ladder that would reach all the way up to Heaven; they reasoned that it wasn't too much in exchange for the whorl.

Again, the man went and beat on the mound. Kidhouse asked as he had before, "Who's that banging on my house?"

And the old man answered once more, "It's your neighbor next door. My old lady wants something for her whorl."

Hearing that, Kidhouse became decidedly annoyed.

"Isn't the blasted whorl ever paid for, then?" he asked.

The old man pleaded with him all the more, saying he wanted to bring dear Saint Mary the leftover pails of porridge. With that, Kidhouse relented, gave him the ladder, and even raised it for him. This pleased the old man very much, and he returned home to his wife.

The two of them then made ready for their trip, taking the pails of porridge with them. But when they had gone quite a long way up the ladder, they began to get dizzy, and the result was that they both fell down and splintered their skulls, the splatters of brains and porridge flying all over the world. And wherever blotches of the old couple's brains landed on stones, they turned into white specks of lichen, while the porridge turned into yellow ones. Both may be seen on rocks even up to this day.

"Strike It While It's Still on My Nose"

Once upon a time there was a king and a queen in their palace and an old man with his crone in a nearby cottage. One day the old couple bought a keg full of butter which they intended to keep for the winter. But they were at a loss where to store it so that no one could steal its contents. Finally, they agreed that they would ask for its safekeeping at the king's court. This was easily obtained; the king said he would store it for them. They put the keg in place themselves and tied a seal over it.

Time now passed until the fall. Then the old woman began to crave the butter, and she soon thought up a scheme to get it. One sunny day she got up early, went in to her husband, and told him she had been summoned to the palace to present a baby at the font, so she would have to go. The man said that was a matter of course.

The crone then dressed in a great hurry and went to the palace. There she said she was supposed to get a pinch of butter from the keg, and people believed her and let her into the storeroom. The woman took a generous layer from the top of the keg and returned home. The man asked her what name they had given the infant at the palace.

"They named her Topsy, a true little lady," she said.

When the old crone had finished what she had taken, she said to her husband one day, "They're summoning me to the palace again."

The man asked for what purpose.

"To present a baby at the font," she said.

"Go then," said the old man.

The woman went to the king's court, saying as she had before that she was to get some butter from the keg. This time, she took butter as far down as the middle. And when she returned home, the man asked what the child was called.

"Middle is her name, a marvel of a girl," she told him.

When the woman had finished this batch, she informed her husband, "They're asking me again to come to the palace and present a baby at the font."

"Go then," said the old man.

Off she went to the palace, saying she was supposed to get some butter. Now she took so much that she could see the groove in the staves. When she returned home again, the man asked the name of the baby.

"Groove they called her, a graceless child," she said.

A long time passed, and the old woman was out of butter once more. Then she said to her spouse, "They're asking for me again at the palace."

"For what purpose?" the man inquired.

"To present a baby at the font," said the crone.

"Then go," he said.

At the palace, the old woman said as before that she was there to get some butter. This time, she took all that was left in the keg. On her return, the man asked her the child's name.

"They named him Bottom, a brawny lad," said the old woman.

110

Time now wore on until late winter. By then, the couple's household began to feel shortage. So the man said to his wife that they had better get their keg of butter from the king's court. The old woman agreed, and they both went to claim their keg. It was given to them, and when they saw the seal had not been tampered with, they rolled the keg home to their cottage. Then the man opened it and found it was totally empty. More than a little taken aback, he asked his wife how on earth that could be. She acted no less surprised than he was and pretended not to know what kind of trick had been played on them. But just at that moment, the old woman saw a large bluebottle that had flown into the keg.

"There's the confounded thief," she said, pointing the fly out to her husband. "Just look at that scoundrel of a fly; it must have eaten up all our butter," she added.

The old man saw that this must be the case. Enraged, he got hold of his sledgehammer, which he used to beat stockfish with, intending to knock the thief dead. He locked the cottage so the fly wouldn't escape and then began pursuing it, striking out at it left and right and breaking everything in sight, but he could never hit the fly.

Finally exhausted, the man sat down, seething with anger. Then the bluebottle came and alighted right on his nose. The man asked the woman to thwack the fly, telling her, "Strike it while it's still on my nose," which has since become a saying. The crone raised the sledgehammer and brought it down with all the strength she could muster on the old man's nose, knocking him dead on the spot. But the bluebottle escaped and has yet to be thwacked. And the crone is still keening over her old husband.

"You're Lucky, God, That I Can't Reach You"

A man and his wife lived on a farm. One summer they had a great deal of hay in the field, most of it half-dry or more, but it looked like rain. So, together with their hired hands, they went to gather the hay before the squalls would soak it. Although they all did their utmost, it just wasn't enough, and the rain descended upon them while a considerable spread of hay was still left. Any further effort was useless.

This made the farmer's wife very angry, both at the rain and at him who gives the rain. She grabbed her rake by the head, or close to the head, and jabbed it up toward the heavens as far as she could, exclaiming, "You're lucky, God, that I can't reach you."

The man let no such angry words fall at the time, but it became obvious the following day that he, too, had been offended by the rain. That day, as it happened, was bright and sunny, and when he entered the *badstofa* in the morning to eat his breakfast, the sun was shining right into his face. The man made short shrift of it, pulled off his pants, and hung them over the window, saying, "You didn't shine so brilliantly on my chew of hay yesterday."

"I Wonder if My Boats Will Go out Today"

The most miserable hovel in the Helgafell parish is called Botn; it never sees sun or summer. A man once lived there, a vagrant creature by the name of Árni. He was known as Árni of Botn.

One day he equipped himself with food and new footwear, loaded his nags, and set off for the South so far that no one had heard of Árni of Botn. He finally came to a large and stately parsonage where he stayed the night. The parson had a pretty, young daughter.

When Árni woke up and looked at the weather in the morning, he muttered aloud to himself, "I wonder if my boats will go out today." He repeated the same or similar words three consecutive mornings. This did not escape the parson and his daughter, who surmised the man had to be some bigwig from the West.

To make a long story short, Árni proposed to the parson's daughter, and she was married to him. After the wedding, they were given a pair of good mounts, and they departed for the West. And at each large farm on their way, the bride would inquire of her husband, "Is that your farm, dear?" And he would answer as often, "No, not yet."

Thus they proceeded for a long, long time until one night, in total darkness, they arrived at a hovel half buried in the ground. Here, Árni dismounted and helped his wife do the same.

"Is that your farm, dearest?" she asked.

"Yes," said Árni.

So saying, he knocked on the door, and his mother, a wrinkled old hag, opened, asking who was there. Árni identified himself and called inside — for it was so dark he couldn't see his hand in front of his face — "Light the candles on the gold candelabra."

"I can't do that," said the old one.

"Then light one in the silver lantern," Árni told her.

"I can't do that either," the crone replied.

"Well, light the goddamn fish-oil lamp, then," he yelled.

"That I'll do," said the hag, running to do so.

Of the married life of Árni and the parson's daughter, nothing has been recorded, but about Árni of Botn, there is the following verse:

> Árni of Botn, ever rotten,
> utterly base and mean.
> A pilferers' lair is his lodgment, where
> the light of the sun is never seen.

"Now I Should Laugh —"

Once there was a married couple who had three daughters. Their names are not recorded, but when they were old enough, they all married, and shortly after that, both parents died, leaving their estate to the daughters. Among other valuables the couple had was a gold ring which all the daughters coveted, but they could not agree who should have it. Finally, they struck a bargain: The one among them who could make the biggest fool of her husband would receive the ring, and they decided to meet at church the following Easter Sunday to compare their tricks.

During Lent, the first one began to prepare for Easter by sitting down to spin, but no one could see what it was that she was spinning. Her husband mentioned this to her, asking what she was doing.

"Can't you see?" she retorted.

"No," he said. "I see you move your hands as if you were spinning, but I don't see any yarn."

"What I'm spinning," said the woman, "is gossamer so fine that no one can see it, and I'm going to make you a suit of it to wear at Easter."

The husband then dropped the matter. When she had finished spinning, she began to weave the gossamer, and after that to sew her husband a suit from it. None of it was ever seen, but she had the suit ready by Easter.

113

As Lent wore on, the second daughter became very downcast and sad. Her husband asked her what was the matter.

"I can't bear to see you so ill," she said.

"Ill? Me?" said the husband. "On the contrary, I'm in the best of health."

"How can you say that?" said the woman. "You're pale and hollow-eyed, and anybody can see you're quite sick."

The husband wouldn't believe her, and they said no more about it for the time being. Shortly afterward, however, she began to lament again how sick he was, and though he asserted he was not, she talked him into going to bed and continued to tell him that he was getting weaker and weaker, while he protested that his health was fine.

This went on until shortly before Easter. Then the woman became absolutely grief-stricken and said to her husband, "Oh, now you're dead."

"I'm not!" said the husband. "I'm as much alive as you or anybody else."

"Oh yes, you're dead all right," said the woman, weeping her eyes out, and she kept this up until she convinced him that he really was dead. Then he was laid out on a bier, and the woman had a coffin made for him to be ready by Easter. It was arranged that he be buried on Easter Sunday.

The third daughter was married to a man whose voice was so dreadful and grating that no one could stand his singing.

When Easter Sunday arrived, the first daughter came up to her husband and began to touch and stroke him, and she fussed about him, all the while telling him that she was dressing him in his gossamer suit. The husband said he felt naked, but she replied it was merely because the suit was so exquisite.

The daughter married to the dead man had him coffined but left him a small hole at the head through which he could see. That done, he was taken to the church.

The third daughter said to her husband, "You'll have to sing in church today, my dear." He replied that the congregation would only break up laughing; she of all people should know, he said.

"But everyone thinks you sing beautifully," answered the woman. And she kept reassuring him of it until he began to believe it. So, once in church, he sang out forcefully, while the rest of the congregation looked at one another and giggled.

Also in church was the man in the gossamer clothes, and when the one in the coffin saw him naked like that and at the same time heard the singing of the other, he could no longer contain himself and exclaimed, "Now I should laugh if I weren't dead!"

Hearing his words, the others realized their folly. The singer stopped in mid-phrase, while the gossamer-clad gentleman scrambled to the door, convinced now of his nakedness. The man in the coffin lay there until the sermon was over, after which he got up. His wife was adjudged to have earned the ring.

And that's the end of this story.

Notes

JÁ=*Íslenzkar þjóðsögur og æfintýri*. Compiled by Jón Árnason. New, enlarged edition prepared by Árni Böðvarsson and Bjarni Vilhjálmsson. Vol. I-VI, Reykjavík 1954-61.

Elves and Trolls

Genesis of the Elves (Huldumanna genesis) JÁ I,7.
"Whatever must be hidden from me...": The common name for elves in Icelandic, *huldufólk*, means precisely "hidden people."

The Field Hand (Kaupamaðurinn) JÁ I,12.
"To know," in Icelandic folklore, usually means knowing magic or witchcraft.

The Magistrate's Wife of Burstarfell (Sýslumannskonan á Burstarfelli) JÁ I,15.
Baðstofa was the common bed- and living-room of the traditional Icelandic farmhouse. Originally a sauna — the word means "bathroom" — it later began to be used for sleeping in cold winters because the stone oven used to produce steam for the bath was easy to heat and retained warmth well. So, little by little, the *baðstofa* became the center of the farmhouse, where people slept, ate, and worked.

The Tunga Bluff (Tungustapi) JÁ I,32.
An abbey that originally had been located on the island of Flatey in Breidafjördur was moved to Helgafell on Snaefellsnes in 1184 and maintained there until the Reformation in the mid-16th century. It was a noted seat of learning where many books that now count as treasures of Icelandic culture were written.

"Father of Eighteen in Elfland" (Átján barna faðir í Álfheimum) JÁ I,43.

The Hired Hand and the Lake Dwellers (Vinnumaðurinn og sæfólkið) JÁ I,112.
It was the custom in former ages that all who were able to would celebrate Christmas mass beginning Christmas Eve and worship (with some interrup-

tions) all through the night until Christmas morning. But someone would always be left behind "house-sitting" — i.e., guarding the farm and tending to the livestock if need be.

Of Marbendill (Frá marbendli) JÁ I,127.
Book of Settlements: a 13th-century account of the settlement of Iceland, listing some 400 of its original settlers, their forebears, and many descendants.

Drangey Consecrated (Vígð Drangey) JÁ I,138.
The "now" of this story, as well as other references to the "present" time (customs, etc.), is of course that of the mid-19th century, when the story was recorded.
The Saga of Grettir is one of the best-known of the Icelandic sagas, written in the early 14th century.
Gudmundur Arason, called the Good, was bishop of the northern bishopric of Hólar in Hjaltadalur from 1203 to 1237. Gvendur is a common diminutive of Gudmundur.

Gissur of Botnar (Gissur á Botnum) JÁ I,151.
Mt. Hekla is Iceland's most famous volcano, which in medieval European superstition was thought to be the back door of Hell. It has erupted numerous times since Iceland was settled, most recently in the early 1980s.
The angelica (*archangelica officinalis*) is an herb of the carrot family, whose root was much used in former times for flavoring and medicinal purposes. It is still used to flavor a certain brand of Icelandic liquor.

Hallgerdur of Bláfell (Hallgerður á Bláfelli) JÁ I,155.
Ólafur asked Hallgerdur to leave his horse "unharmed" because there were thought to be instances when horses had foundered after they were taken by trolls, either to ease their travels or to cross rivers. Such horses were said to be "troll-ridden."

Gilitrutt (Gilitrutt) JÁ I,172.

The Night-Troll (Nátttröllið) JÁ I,198.
For guarding the farm on Christmas Eve, see "The Hired Hand and the Lake Dwellers," above.
Badstofa: see above, "The Magistrate's Wife of Burstarfell."
It was the nature of night trolls that they were light-shy and turned into stone if caught by daylight.

"Deep Indeed the Iceland Channels" (Djúpir eru Íslands álar) JÁ I,206.

Ghosts and Sorcerers

"Mother in the Pen, Pen" (Móðir mín í kví, kví) JÁ I,217.
Little is now known of the *vikivaki* dance, as indeed of other popular Icelandic dances of old.
It was thought to be a characteristic of ghostly speech that it often repeated the last word of a clause, especially when in verse, cf. "The Deacon of Myrká," below.

"Give Me Back My Bone, Gunna" (Fáðu mér beinið mitt, Gunna) JÁ I,229.
Gunna is a common diminutive of the girl's name, Gudrún.

"Gone Is My Glowing Skin Tone" (Horfinn er fagur farfi) JÁ I,233.

The Ghost and the Cash Box (Draugurinn og peningakistillinn) JÁ I,258.
Moving Days: generally, the first four days in the seventh week of summer, beginning anytime from May 31 to June 6. During these days, moving from one farm to another was supposed to take place, and hired people would begin their service.

The Deacon of Myrká (Djákninn á Myrká) JÁ I,270.
Garún: Because the girl's name, Gudrún, contains the Icelandic word for God — *gud* — the ghost could not utter it unchanged; hence Garún. See, however, "Give Me Back My Bone, Gunna," above, for a perfectly good alternative that the ghost could have used. Also, note the repetition in the ghost's speech, cf. "Mother in the Pen, Pen," above.

The Wizards of the Westman Islands (Galdramennirnir í Vestmannaeyjum) JÁ I,308.
The Black Death devastated Iceland in the years 1402-04.
Sending: literally, anything sent, but in folk belief someone conjured up from the dead and sent to pursue and harm a targeted victim.

Rusty of Írafell (Írafells-Móri) JÁ I,364.
Sending: see "The Wizards of the Westman Islands," above.
Skyr: an Icelandic dairy product similar to yogurt or sour cream.
Passion Hymns: a cycle of 50 hymns relating to the passion of Christ, written by the Rev. Hallgrímur Pétursson (1614-74) and considered one of the gems of Icelandic literature.
Badstofa: see "The Magistrate's Wife of Burstarfell," above.

Tales of Saemundur the Learned
Saemundur Sigfússon, called the Learned, is a historical personage, who lived from 1056 to 1133. At one time, he was erroneously thought to have been

the compiler of *The Poetic Edda*, hence the occasional reference to it as *Saemundur-Edda*. His benefice, centered at Oddi in the Rangárvalla County, became in his day a noted seat of learning, where the great historiographer Snorri Sturluson (1179-1241) grew up with Saemundur's grandson, Jón Loftsson.

1. The Black School (Svartiskóli) JÁ I,475.
The Black School is generally thought to be the University of Paris, known as the Sorbonne.
"Once there were three Icelanders together...": In this instance, the folk imagination has taken a great leap across the ages, for Saemundur the Learned and the Rev. Hálfdan of Fell (d. 1568?) were separated by no less than four centuries.

2. How Saemundur Got His Benefice (Sæmundur fróði fær Oddann) JÁ I,478.
"...applied to the king...": continuation of the anachronism in the previous tale. In Saemundur's day, Iceland was a commonwealth with no king. In any case, the king would have had nothing to do with the granting of church offices until after the Reformation, which in Iceland occurred in the mid-16th century.

3. Gathering the Hay (Heyhirðingin) JÁ I,478.
"To know": see note to "The Field Hand," above.
It is a mark of the popular reverence for Saemundur's learning that he was supposed to have Satan himself at his service, as it were, and be able to order him around as he pleased.

4. The Imp Whistle (Púkablístran) JÁ I,479.

5. The Imp and the Cowherd (Púkinn og fjósamaðurinn) JÁ I,481.

6. Old Nick's Pact With the Weaver (Kaup Kölska við vefjarkonuna) JÁ I,482.
Cake: This refers to an unleavened bread, somewhat like a Middle Eastern pita, usually called *flatkaka*, or "flat cake."

Tales of the Reverend Eiríkur of Vogsósar
The Rev. Eiríkur Magnússon is a historical personage who lived from c. 1638 to 1716.
Note the similarity between the Rev. Eiríkur's weekly disappearance and that of Sveinn in "The Tunga Bluff," who vanished every New Year's Eve.

1. How Eiríkur Learned Magic in School (Eiríkur nemur kunnáttu í skóla) JÁ I,543.
Letter: This, of course, refers to a magic letter, not one of the Latin alphabet.

2. The Bull (Tarfurinn) JÁ I,547.

3. The Horse Theft (Hestastuldurinn) JÁ I,548.

Saints and Sinners

Satan Went to Make a Man (Skrattinn fór að skapa mann) JÁ II,7.

The Imp on the Church Beam (Púkinn á kirkjubitanum) JÁ II,8.

The Dance at Hruni (Dansinn í Hruna) JÁ II,11.

The Parish Pauper (Niðursetukerlingin) JÁ II,17.

The Ptarmigan (Rjúpan) JÁ II,27.

My Jón's Soul (Sálin hans Jóns míns) JÁ II,42.
This story, recorded by the Rev. Matthías Jochumsson (1835-1920), one of Iceland's leading 19th-century poets, was an inspiration to another prominent poet, Davíd Stefánsson (1895-1964), who used it both for a long humorous poem and a popular play, *The Golden Gate*.

Úlfur's Lake (Úlfsvatn) JÁ II,164.

An Outlaw Killed (Drepinn útilegumaður) JÁ II,168.
The Haze Hardships, which began with the eruption of Laki in 1783, were so called because of a blue haze, caused by fine ash dust and gases from the eruption, that hung over the country in the summer of 1783. The Haze Hardships killed more than 20% of the human population of Iceland and about 75% of the nation's livestock.
"...head by his buttocks...": It was the folk belief that if a dead man's head was placed by his buttocks, he would then be unable to return and haunt the living.

"Up, My Six, in the Name of Jesus" (Upp mínir sex í Jesú nafni) JÁ II,170.
"...helping them off with their wet clothes...": It was part of common hospitality that a maid help the guest undress at night, especially if his clothes were wet. She would then see to it that they were dry for him in the morning.

Bjarni Sveinsson and His Sister Salvör (Bjarni Sveinsson og Salvör systir hans) JÁ II,189.
Iceland moss (*cetraria islandica*) is a lichen, which in former days — and to some extent even today — was much used as a food plant. It is rich in vitamins.
"...helped him take off his wet clothes...": see note to the preceding story, "Up, My Six, in the Name of Jesus."
Moving Days: see note to "The Ghost and the Cash Box," above.

Visitation by the Bishop of Skálholt (Vísitazíuferð Skálholtsbiskups) JÁ II,246.

Badstofa: see note to "The Magistrate's Wife of Burstarfell," above.

Althing: the Icelandic parliament, the oldest legislative body in the world, established in 930. It used to convene for about two weeks in June every year at Thingvellir in the South. At that time, traders, entertainers, and sundry other people who had nothing to do with the functions of the Althing would flock to Thingvellir to see other people, hear news, and conclude social or business affairs.

Miscellaneous Tales

The Grímsey Man and the Polar Bear (Grímseyingurinn og bjarndýrið) JÁ I,606.

Polar bears are not denizens of Iceland but occasionally drift over there with floating ice.

Tale of a Raven (Krummasaga) JÁ I,614.

"...the farm raven...": It was a folk belief that the ravens of each district held an "assembly" in the fall, at which each one was assigned a certain farm to help it (i.e., the raven) survive the winter. Assembly or not, the fact was that the same raven would hover around the same farm all winter long, living off whatever scraps people would throw to it and whatever else it could scrounge up.

Bishop Gudmundur: see note to "Drangey Consecrated," above, as well as the tale itself.

The Sealskin (Selshamurinn) JÁ I,629.

The Serpent of Lagarfljót (Ormurinn í Lagarfljóti) JÁ I,635.

Ling snake: a creation of the folk imagination — there have never been snakes of any sort in Iceland — probably influenced by the story of Fáfnir and the Rheingold.

Two Finns: The designation was often used to mean the Lapps, who had a reputation of being eminently able sorcerers.

The Convent at Kirkjubaer (Kirkjubæjarklaustur) JÁ II,76.

Book of Settlements: see note to "Of Marbendill," above.

Papar: Irish hermits who are said to have been in Iceland before the arrival of the Norse settlers.

"...a mile and a quarter away...": This is probably meant to be either Danish (German) miles, which would make the distance close to six English miles, or Norwegian miles, which would mean nearly nine English ones. In reality, however, the distance is more than 20 English miles.

Striders: The name, people believe, refers to the sisters' eagerness to meet with the brothers from Thykkvibaer; that is, they would walk with long strides.

The River Öxará (Öxará) JÁ II,83.
Öxará is the stream that flows through Thingvellir — Assembly Plains —
the site of the Icelandic parliament, Althing, until 1800. See also note to
"Visitation by the Bishop of Skálholt," above.

The Story of Prince Hlini (Sagan af Hlina kóngssyni) JÁ II,412.

Búkolla and the Boy (Búkolla og strákurinn) JÁ II,445.

"My Old Lady Wants Something for Her Whorl" (Kerling vill hafa nokkuð
fyrir snúð sinn) JÁ II,479.

"Strike It While It's Still on My Nose" (Neyttu á meðan á nefinu stendur)
JÁ II,481.

"You're Lucky, God, That I Can't Reach You" (Þú nýtur þess guð, að ég
næ ekki til þín) JÁ II,497.
Badstofa: see note to "The Magistrate's Wife of Burstarfell."

"I Wonder if My Boats Will Go out Today" (Skyldu bátar mínir róa í dag?)
JÁ II,499.

"Now I Should Laugh —" (Nú skyldi ég hlæja) JÁ V,427.